C000216015

By the same author

LISTENING AND HELPING IN THE WORKPLACE

CRITICAL INCIDENT DEBRIEFING

Understanding and
Dealing with Trauma

FRANK PARKINSON

A Condor Book
Souvenir Press (E&A) Ltd

First published 1997 by Souvenir Press,
(Educational & Academic) Ltd,
43 Great Russell Street, London WC1B 3PA
and simultaneously in Canada

ISBN 0 285 63372 4

Photoset by Rowland Phototypesetting Ltd,
Bury St Edmunds, Suffolk
Printed and bound in Great Britain by
Creative Print and Design (Wales), Ebbw Vale

Contents

Summaries and Check-lists

Preface

I had planned to write a book on Critical Incident Debriefing which, after an explanatory introduction, would offer a series of chapters outlining the Debriefing model. However, when I started to write, I soon realised that it was not going to be quite so simple. Many questions began to arise, deriving both from my experience and from my belief that those who wish to understand or conduct Debriefing need a wide knowledge of a number of subjects. Also, the concept of Debriefing raises many pertinent issues that I felt it necessary to discuss.

The first question concerned the nature and development of traumatic reactions and the need to ask why they occur. To this there is no definitive answer, although there are models that can further our understanding. The subject of Debriefing also raised questions not only about the nature of traumatic incidents, but also about the personalities, previous experiences and training of those involved, and the support they might receive both during and after the incident. Furthermore, I felt it was important to look at the nature of post-traumatic stress (PTS) and at the development of post-traumatic stress disorder (PTSD), because those who conduct Debriefing sessions need to have a clear understanding of these conditions. Next, I asked, how do those who are involved in traumatic incidents, especially professionals, cope? This led me to consider the various strategies that people use as coping mechanisms, and why some appear to cope better than others.

Then, in order to understand the treatment offered to those who are involved in traumatic incidents, I needed to look at the influences of war and other disasters on the understanding and definition of trauma, and at some of the theories underpinning treatment. I have also considered some of the vast amount of research material available in the field. No doubt, by the time this book is published there will be yet more, and some of the information given here will be out of date. Understanding traumatic reactions is still in its infancy, and research results are controversial and sometimes contradictory. If you wish to delve further into the subject, consider joining the European Society for Traumatic Stress Studies (address on page 268).

Another question concerned the common beliefs, shared by therapists, counsellors and helpers, that underpin the *kind* of help they offer to those who suffer. Does talking about traumatic experiences help? If so, how should those offering support go about it? Should a structure be imposed, or should it be left to the person experiencing the trauma to say whatever he wishes, when he wishes? Most therapists believe that talking does help, and Critical Incident Debriefing is based on the belief that this talking needs to be structured cognitively.

The early methods evolved by Jeffrey Mitchell incorporating demobilisation, defusing and Debriefing, and their origins, were my next focus. A chapter on defusing was clearly necessary because many organisations, the employers of those who experience trauma in the course of their professional duties, are now using it as a preliminary to, or instead of, Debriefing. Then, what about the qualifications that debriefers need, and how should they be trained and supported? How should a Debriefing be organised? It seemed important to consider all of this before discussing in detail the revised model of Debriefing—the main subject of this book. This model has been used almost exclusively after sudden traumatic incidents, and so the last chapter looks at how it has been applied and adapted in different situations and with different people. I also thought it a good idea to include a shortened version of the revised model (Appendix A) for those who may want to use it, and a list of treatment and training centres (Appendix B); and Appendix C offers a comprehensive list of references and further reading.

I hope that this book will help people to understand the Debriefing process, how it came to be, and what it can offer to those who experience trauma. But I do not intend it to be used as a substitute for sound training in Debriefing. Mitchell sees Debriefing as a method that should be under the direction of 'mental health professionals' assisted by peer support personnel, but I do not believe that Debriefing is the exclusive prerogative of medical personnel. Outside the USA, Debriefing is used by counsellors, therapists, psychologists, welfare officers, psychiatrists and occupational health personnel. Some debrief on their own, while others have a co-debriefer present. What is important is that debriefers should be carefully selected and thoroughly trained. It would be wrong for anyone, no matter how well qualified as a professional counsellor or therapist, to attempt to conduct Debriefing sessions without some basic training. Debriefers should measure up to certain criteria: in addition to being thoroughly trained in the model, they should have an understanding of PTS reactions and of PTSD; possess good basic listening and responding skills; be able to work with individuals as well as with groups; work under a recognised code of ethics such as those of the British Association for Counselling or the British Psychological Society; be under personal and group supervision and, where necessary, have personal indemnity insurance (see pages 124–8). Furthermore, debriefers should not attempt to train others before they have gained a wide experience of Debriefing—Mitchell argues that experience of at least twenty-five Debriefings is called for.

So, although it can be used as a training handbook, to encourage discussion and to give information, this is not a do-it-yourself book. Mitchell refers to the model as the 'Critical Incident Stress Debriefing' and Atle Dyregrov calls it 'Psychological Debriefing'. Here it is generally referred to as 'Critical Incident Debriefing'. Sometimes the word 'client' or 'clients' is used in the sense of those who are debriefed, but they are usually referred to as 'debriefees'. Debriefers may, of course, be either male or female, and if there is a preponderance here of one over the other, it is for the sake of continuity—'he' and 'she' are interchangeable. The specific cases included are based on real people and real incidents but, while the facts of both incidents and reactions remain unaltered, some of the details have been changed in order to protect the identities of those involved.

I would like to thank the many colleagues who have encouraged and supported me, especially by discussing with me their use of, and success with, the model. I thank my wife, who has also supported me, and offered helpful comments on the manuscript. I am grateful to Jeffrey Mitchell and Atle Dyregrov for initiating and developing Debriefing; and I also remember with gratitude Janet Johnston from the Dover Counselling Centre, who first introduced me to the model.

Introduction

Critical Incident Debriefing began in the United States in the early 1980s with the work of Dr Jeffrey Mitchell, after the experience of many different types of civilian disaster for which methods based on crisis intervention theory were being developed. Mitchell worked as a fire-officer paramedic, but is now Clinical Associate Professor of the Emergency Health Services at the University of Maryland. His book on Critical Incident Stress Debriefing (Mitchell and Everly 1995) outlines his model, and it has developed and evolved following the work of Dr Atle Dyregrov from the University of Bergen in Norway. It has been further modified by others, without any change in the basic structure, for use in many different types of situation; this book outlines and explains the three-stage model based on the Facts–Feelings–Future structure.

Critical Incident Debriefing is not a cure for post-traumatic stress or an injection against the development of post-traumatic stress disorder. Nor does it suggest that all who are involved in traumatic incidents are suffering or will suffer and need help. It is a method of intervention that attempts to reduce the degree of traumatic reactions, and is designed as part of the normal procedure to be followed when traumatic incidents have occurred. It assumes that after traumatic incidents most people will cope, but that they will recover more quickly if they have a structured procedure to follow which enables them to talk through what has happened and how they have reacted. Critical Incident Debriefing is not counselling, but a cognitively based model which aims to help those involved to integrate the incident into their experience and into their lives.

It is sometimes suggested that counsellors and therapists travel from disaster to disaster, actively looking for clients—so-called

'ambulance-chasers', asking people how they feel and implying
that they do, should and will have problems. Such a suggestion
reveals a lack of understanding both of the nature of trauma and
of how people can be helped. During and immediately after an
incident victims and rescuers need not counselling or Debriefing,
but support, and to be allowed to get on with the task of surviving
or of rescuing people and saving lives. When the incident is over,
they often need further support and information, preferably from
those familiar to them. Critical Incident Debriefing is used a few
days after the incident, when people are usually more willing and
able to talk. Hopefully, Debriefing will help them to make some
sense of the event and of their own involvement; and to prepare
them for the future and reassure them that their reactions to
trauma are the normal reactions of normal people to abnormal
events—not signs of weakness or inadequacy.

My own journey in discovering, using and developing the
model came from necessity and from a request for help. In 1989
I was invited to help some young military recruits who had given
assistance immediately after an air crash and were quite distressed
by what they had found and had to do. I was not sure how to
approach this, but used my knowledge of counselling skills and
of bereavement, loss and stress reactions to construct a programme. This consisted of a short talk on the normality of stress
and traumatic reactions, followed by videos showing major disasters and the possible effects on individuals. I then asked those
attending to assemble into small groups and discuss various questions about the incident and their reactions to it. This proved to
be very difficult for them; in particular, the men were very resistant to discussing anything about their involvement. This, I
thought, was probably due to a strong military macho image and
to the fact that young women were present. Unlike the men, most
of the women were able to talk quite freely about how they felt.
At the end I gave a summary of the session, as well as a short
talk on possible future reactions and the availability of various
individuals and agencies who might help, should help be needed.
I left with a feeling that this had not been the best thing I had
ever done, but the Commanding Officer rang me some days later

to say how helpful many had said it had been. However, I still felt that, though this counselling approach had helped in some small way, I should have used a more structured and systematic method and model.

A few months later, after the riots early in 1990, I was asked to help some members of staff from Strangeways Prison in Manchester. Through Janet Johnston of the Dover Counselling Centre I had read some of the work of Jeffrey Mitchell and Atle Dyregrov on Debriefing. I contacted Dyregrov, who encouraged me to use the model. I met up with the Strangeways team in the peaceful atmosphere of a retreat house on the edge of the Forest of Bowland in North Lancashire. I divided the model into its usual seven sections, scheduling it with the team over a period of two days, and I found that it provided a logical and structured method of dealing with the riots and people's reactions to them.

The Critical Incident Debriefing model was more helpful, both for me and for the participants, than a general counselling approach would have been. We were able to set the scene and discuss confidentiality and how we were going to conduct the sessions, then work slowly through their individual stories without allowing feelings and emotional reactions to interfere unduly. We looked at what they had expected and at what had actually happened, and at their thoughts and impressions. They were then allowed to express their emotional reactions and to talk about their feelings. The session concluded with a presentation on possible future reactions—an educational input that explained their reactions to them, reassured them that these had been normal, and outlined what help was available should they need it. The fact that all this was done in the relaxing surroundings of an old abbey was, I believe, an extra bonus.

I felt I had used a new and exciting approach which had provided a safe and relatively simple model for helping this group of people who had been through a long traumatic experience. Some had been affected more than others, but all responded to the model and were able to talk. As a counsellor trained in the psychodynamic model, I found this method of working different from my usual one, but it had felt exactly right. I had known precisely what procedure to follow, and the model had provided an umbrella of safety under which we could all work. If in doubt, stick to the model, was my rule.

I did not need to explore the backgrounds of these people or delve into their childhoods and previous experiences, but could simply ask them to concentrate on the incident and their reactions to it. Previous experiences, attitudes and beliefs were important, and some emerged, but the main focus was on the here and now and on present reactions to the incident in which those reactions had originated. In addition, we focused on the future, on their ability to identify and strengthen their own group solidarity and coping mechanisms, and on resources for helping. It was of particular significance that many of the group were clergy: the riots took place over a period which included Easter, and some felt that they could not celebrate the Resurrection because the riots had made them feel that they were still experiencing their own Good Friday and were unable to move forward.

Since then I have adapted and used the Debriefing method with individuals, with couples, and with both small and large groups after many different kinds of incident. I have used it with helpers, rescuers and immediate victims after:

- Air crashes and riots.
- Fatal traffic accidents and fatal shootings.
- The Baltic Exchange bombing.
- Hostage situations.
- Suicide, rape and assault.
- War and combat experience.
- Armed robberies and violence.
- The return of aid workers from Rwanda, Bosnia, Somalia and the Sudan.
- Accidents at work.

Some of these incidents were short-lived and others lasted many months. It is relatively easy to conduct a Debriefing after a sudden event, but when an event stretches over a long period— perhaps in a hostage situation, or in the case of aid workers spending many months overseas, or of police, fire and rescue and ambulance personnel who may experience on-going levels of trauma—then it is more difficult. But although each session has to be structured in a different way, the Debriefing procedure used is the same. To deal with extended traumatic experiences, significant incidents can be brought forward into the present experiences and needs of the debriefees. The model can also be used within a counselling framework: here clients are debriefed by asking them to look at the facts first and then the feelings. One of the values of the model lies in the flexibility and adaptability of the Facts–Feelings–Future structure (discussed later in the book).

My experience in this area leads me firmly to believe that this method of intervention does help individuals and groups to cope with the aftermath of traumatic incidents. My evidence for this is anecdotal and experiential: individuals tell me that it helps them to integrate and understand the event and their emotional reactions to it; groups tell me that as the result of a Debriefing they feel a much stronger sense of solidarity, belonging and mutual support.

A very experienced police officer who was debriefed after a traumatic incident said, 'This is the best thing I have done in all my twenty years of service. We should have had this years ago.'

This comment has been echoed over and over again by many different people after many different incidents. Within organisations I have occasionally experienced some initial resistance and scepticism towards the method, but eventually people begin to ask for a Debriefing because others have told them that it has helped. Amongst other groups, this has happened with the police, building societies and aid agencies. Because colleagues have spoken positively about their own Debriefing, aid workers returning from overseas have asked, 'When are we having ours?'

There is, at present, a lack of definitive research evidence to show how effective this method is. Some have said that their research suggests that those who are debriefed fare no better or worse than those who are not (Raphael and Meldrum 1995). But it must be remembered that research into Debriefing is very difficult because of the many variables involved: the nature, timing and duration of the incident; the characters, personalities and previous life experiences of the individuals, their susceptibility to react, and their vulnerability; the training or preparation they have received; the support given during and after the incident; the skill of the debriefer; the ways the questions are framed and asked; uncertainty about possible future reactions. And these are only some of the problems.

We also need to ask what research methods were used, which Debriefing model, when, by whom and with whom. Was the method used consistently? Was it conducted by the same people in the same way and with similar people involved in the same incident? When questions were asked at a later stage, were those who had been debriefed more aware of their reactions than those who had not been, and were those who had not been debriefed more resistant to either discussing or admitting to having any reactions? Can research show what might or might not have developed in the case of any given individual, whether debriefed or not, and, in concentrating on levels of reactions, is the research measuring the right things? Debriefing is not a precise science that can be conducted every time under exactly the same conditions. Furthermore, some who say that they use Debriefing do not use the Mitchell and Dyregrov models, but methods more akin to counselling which are not as structured as Critical Incident Debriefing.

In spite of its basis in crisis intervention theory, cognitive–behavioural methods and other theories and therapies, there is concern that it is not clear if and how Debriefing works, what it does for and to people, and whether it is suitable for everyone. It is often commented that Debriefing may result in re-traumatisation, but in over seven years' experience of conducting Debriefings after many different incidents, with both individuals and groups, I have never found this to happen. Individuals have re-experienced powerful reactions and feelings deriving from the original trauma and sometimes from other traumas, both past and present, but always in a safe and supportive environment and in a way which enables them to cope.

Although the research is inconclusive, it is interesting to note that many—including those writing in the *British Medical Journal* article mentioned above (Raphael and Meldrum 1995)—who have said that Debriefing may not be any more effective than other methods of intervention, say that it should nonetheless be used because those who are debriefed feel and believe that it helps.

I firmly believe that Debriefing is a process that can help those who experience trauma to survive and cope better, not just by encouraging and enabling them to express their feelings and emotions, but by helping them to integrate the event into their lives. Also, the possibility of reactions or symptoms either developing or becoming worse is likely to be reduced. If they can achieve these aims through Debriefing, those who experience traumatic events should be better able to make sense of what they have experienced and move forward in their lives.

1 The Development of Traumatic Reactions

WHY DO REACTIONS OCCUR?

Psychological reactions to traumatic incidents can be anything from mildly disturbing and temporary to dramatic, disabling and persistent. Some people appear to have no reactions other than calmness and acceptance, while others experience feelings, emotions and symptoms which can last from a few minutes to hours, days or months. While most people recover and return to their normal functioning within a short while, some find that their reactions persist and begin to affect their health and their relationships at home and at work, influencing the whole of their lives. At worst, their health deteriorates and they lose interest in life generally and are unable to work or sustain meaningful and stable relationships. Moreover, reactions can be delayed, and some will discover that memories, feelings and emotions, which they thought were forgotten, surface many years later—sometimes with devastating effect. A few will develop deeper and more distressing symptoms, such that post-traumatic stress disorder (or syndrome) will be diagnosed.

It is not certain why reactions occur to traumatic events, but they appear to be influenced by at least three variables:

1 The traumatic nature of the incident.
2 The character and personality of the individual involved.
3 The preparation of the individual, and the support given before, during and after the incident.

1   The traumatic nature of the incident

Intensity of the threat

There are many incidents that are neither life-threatening nor
horrific, yet result in anything from mild to extreme traumatic
reactions. It seems reasonable to assume that the intensity and
distressing nature of the incident must contribute to the way in
which those involved react. The more distressing the incident,
the more likely that their reactions will be at the extreme end of
the spectrum; and a less distressing incident should produce less
distressing reactions. But this is not always the case. Many seemingly simple incidents occur to which the reactions are disturbing.

> In an attempted armed robbery in a small branch of a bank, nobody
> was injured or even faced the robber. When he walked in, no one
> was present behind the tills or even in that section of the building.
> He was seen from behind a one-way screen and, because they were
> suspicious, members of staff did not emerge to serve him. One young
> woman looked round the door and he beckoned her over, but she
> backed away, still watching him. He put a note and a plastic bag
> under the safety screen, but still nobody came forward. Eventually
> he walked out of the branch, but as he did so he turned round and
> made firm eye contact with the woman who had peered round the
> door. The incident was over in about three minutes.

It was thought that, because no one had been injured or had
even faced the robber, everyone was fine and that psychological
help through Debriefing was not needed. But when the Debriefing was conducted, the young woman who had watched him
became highly distressed, saying that she had felt that he had
marked her by 'that look'. She was convinced that he had followed her home. She had got up in the middle of the night to
check the doors and windows, and next morning thought that he
had followed her to work and was waiting to 'get her' at some
time in the future. As she spoke, she was shaking with terror.
The young woman was deeply religious, had previously appeared
to be stable and confident, had no apparent problems, and
belonged to a loving and supportive family. A simple enough

incident, apparently, yet her reactions seemed out of proportion to what had happened.

Pearlin *et al.* (1981) found that there was little relationship between the level of trauma induced and the traumatic nature of the incident. On the other hand, it does seem likely that the reactions of someone who witnesses a mugging or other violent incident will be less strong than those of the immediate victim. A police officer attending a road traffic accident in which people are injured will probably react more strongly if he finds there the mangled body of a child. And his reactions may be even stronger if he has children of his own with whom he identifies the body. Thus, Pearlin's research findings notwithstanding, an incident generating high levels of horror and carnage seems more likely to produce a stronger response than one where these are low. Also, extremely traumatic incidents may strengthen defence mechanisms and produce a greater degree of denial and avoidance behaviour, with the result that those involved claim not to be affected in any way. What may result later from these hidden reactions is another question. However, some people do appear not to be affected by traumatic events in any way whatsoever and cope very well, saying, for instance, 'It hasn't disturbed or upset me in the least', 'Life must go on', 'These things happen and you have to get on with life', 'It's just part of my job', or 'You have to take a positive attitude.'

Other research shows that certain incidents and experiences can be more disturbing than others. A report by Ursano *et al.* (1994) suggests that the risk of PTSD developing increases sevenfold where there is high exposure to combat. Kulk *et al.* (1990) suggest that, in combat experience, exposure to abusive violence—which involves witnessing atrocities and grotesque deaths—produces the highest level of reactions and PTSD. Meichenbaum (1994) says that 70 per cent of torture victims later develop PTSD. And according to McCann and Pearlman (1990), events which are sudden, unexpected and out of the ordinary are more likely to be interpreted as traumatic and result in reactions typical of PTS.

Duration

It is important to consider the length of the incident. Is it short-lived, over in seconds, like a mugging? Or is it long and drawn-out like a hostage situation, or the experience of combat or torture? The longer and more shocking an incident, the more likely are the symptoms to be difficult to deal with, persistent and deeply ingrained. All the same, as in the case of attempted robbery quoted above, an apparently minor and short-lived incident can produce major symptoms.

Meichenbaum (1994) suggests that the reactions of victims of long-term trauma, called 'type 2 stressors', can exceed those of post-traumatic stress disorder. This is a category called 'disorders of extreme stress' (DES), of which the reactions are difficulty in controlling anger, severe mood changes and self-destructive behaviour; depersonalisation, and dissociation from feelings and from the critical event; psychosomatic reactions; extreme or chronic levels of guilt, shame and self-blame; abandonment of previously held beliefs and a desire for revenge; descent into a permanent-victim state and being unable to trust anyone; despair and hopelessness (van der Kolk *et al.* 1991).

Neither the intensity of the threat nor the duration of the incident is necessarily a good indicator of reaction levels and, in some cases, the research seems to present contradictory results. However, with an incident that is highly traumatic and stressful, reactions are likely to be intense, even though defences and denial may be strong and result in reactions being hidden, controlled or repressed.

2   The character and personality of the individual

Different people react to incidents in different ways, and there may be certain common factors as to why this is so, such as personal characteristics and previous traumatic experience, the timing of the event in the life of the person concerned, the question of whether the trauma is on-going, and his or her attitudes and beliefs.

Personal background and life experiences

Some research in the USA suggests a correlation between those who develop symptoms of PTSD and their backgrounds and previous life experiences. Some early behaviours and experiences which seem to predispose a person to developing PTSD are truancy, lying, vandalism, early sexual experience and being in trouble with the police through substance abuse, theft or delinquency (Helzer *et al.* 1987). Research also suggests that of those who developed PTSD during and after the Vietnam War 66 per cent had a family or personal history of psychiatric or mental problems (Davidson, Swartz and Storck 1985). Learned coping strategies, and attitudes and beliefs formed within the family and social environment, will determine to some extent how individuals react to trauma. A person who has learned to react by totally suppressing his feelings may well react in this way to trauma in the future.

> A young man was brought up to believe very firmly that 'men don't cry'. When his pet rabbit and then his grandmother died, he was told that he must not cry, so he didn't. When he married and his baby died, he continued to use the same mechanisms he had learned as a child. He suppressed his feelings and could not understand why his wife was so upset.

But reactions are not as simple, predictable or inevitable as this might suggest. It might have been that when his baby died this man's distress was so extreme that it shattered his defences and he broke down, feeling that he was weak and a failure for not coping. Alternatively, somebody who already has feelings of low self-esteem might react to trauma either by developing an even lower self-esteem and a greater sense of inadequacy (McCann *et al.* 1988), or by compensating via aggression or an exaggerated belief in his own capabilities, confidence and invulnerability.

Experience of previous or present trauma

When someone has experienced a previous trauma, or is already going through one when the critical incident occurs, there is a possibility that any additional traumatic reactions will be intensified. Experience shows that during and after Critical Incident Debriefings previous or present traumas can be resurrected or intensified by the event and by the Debriefing procedure.

A woman became very upset and began to cry during a Debriefing because her feelings about her mother's death a year earlier were coming to the surface. In another incident, a young woman became distressed because she could vividly recall the death of her baby over three years earlier. A building society manager recalled with great anguish an incident, seven years in the past, when he had been threatened by a knife. Another woman found that her legs began to shake uncontrollably because she felt she was back in a car crash she had experienced five years previously.

A young woman involved in an armed robbery had to seek counselling after the Debriefing. Her feelings and reactions to the event were exacerbated and intensified because she was having difficulties with her marriage. Extremely unhappy, she was moving through a very painful time in her life to an almost certain separation and divorce.

Those who have previously been bereaved, divorced, depressed, involved in a traffic accident, made redundant, raped, assaulted or abused, or who have been in any kind of earlier traumatic incident, are probably more susceptible to strong reactions than those who have not. The same may be true of those who are experiencing any of these in the present. And reactions to previous or present traumas may cause some people to repress more strongly any feelings about or reactions to the new trauma, as a defence against experiencing them.

Timing of the incident

The timing of the incident in the life of the individual should also be considered. A police officer may be more vulnerable when he is about to go off duty than at the beginning of his shift. If he is feeling relaxed on his way back to the station to finish duty, he may be less alert, less vigilant. If he is surrounded by supporting colleagues he may be less likely to believe that he is at risk. A bank teller may be more at risk just before the branch closes than when first going on duty. Later in the day she may be beginning to relax, looking forward to going to the cinema or to a disco that evening, anticipating the weekend, or expecting to go on holiday soon. Even the time of day or of the week can determine to some extent a person's frame of mind, and whether or not she is alert and aware or relaxed and unprepared. If she is alert and prepared she may cope better with a traumatic experience than if she is tired and the incident is unexpected and sudden. Age, too, can be a significant factor in determining reactions. A child or young person may be unable to express emotions and feelings verbally, and may react to trauma by becoming withdrawn and anxious or aggressive and violent in his play and relationships.

On-going experience of trauma

The effects of long-term, on-going or intermittent exposure to traumatic incidents are experienced by many professionals, including doctors and nurses, ambulance, fire and rescue and police officers, and military personnel—whether as individuals or as groups. An ambulance officer, in one day alone, can go from a suicide to an imminent birth, then on to a fatal road traffic accident, followed by a heart attack, a cot death or another suicide. This is no simple exposure to traumatic incident, but compound, on-going, in that the individual moves from one traumatic event to another over a relatively short period. The same can be true for aid workers overseas, and for hostages: exposure to stress and trauma may continue for days, months or even years. The effect can be cumulative, with the reservoir of traumatic experience building up as time passes. Resistance and defence mechanisms aimed at suppressing and controlling reactions can reach breaking-point.

A police officer who regularly experienced traumatic incidents said that in the area where he worked this was common and accepted and he had always coped. 'You always get a bit of a punch-up on Saturday nights. It's par for the course.' He had regularly been pushed over, hit, harassed and verbally and physically abused. One Saturday evening, after he had once more been assaulted, he felt that he could no longer cope: he couldn't go to work, was frightened and withdrawn, and had to seek psychiatric and counselling help.

Such a breaking-point can take weeks, months or years to develop and those concerned find that they gradually become isolated and depressed and that their feelings are numbed, or that they become angry, aggressive or violent. Some have described going through a 'trauma barrier', when they begin to behave recklessly or become unable to make reasonable decisions, or any decisions at all. They may move into 'burn-out' or experience what is often called a 'nervous breakdown'. Whatever reactions result from continuous or intermittent exposure to trauma, the quality of life and ability to cope of the individual or group may be seriously impaired. This is sometimes referred to as prolonged duress stress disorder or PDSD.

Attitudes and beliefs
It is possible that someone who firmly believes that events happen because of the will of God or of Allah, or through fate, luck or chance, will accept more readily whatever happens to him in life. If he also believes that God wills it for a purpose, then he will look for some meaning in any given event, and probably find it. If he does *not* find meaning, he may either abandon the belief or adjust it to correlate with his experience.

A woman who had a mentally handicapped child and who thought that she was being punished by God, was told by a religious friend that God only chooses 'special people' to have such children. She found this acceptable, for it meant that she had been specially chosen by God to look after her baby. This seemed to help her to live with this on-going traumatic experience. Part of the difficulty she faced was that she had been sexually abused as a child by an uncle, had developed a low self-esteem, suffered from severe depression and had a highly critical and unsupportive husband. However, the belief that she and her child were special helped her to cope.

A deeply religious man whose wife died believed that her death was the will of God, and his friends told him that it had a purpose. Earlier, others had told him to pray and that prayer could heal her, so that when she died he felt that he had not prayed hard enough or had enough faith. Some even told him that perhaps she had died because of something she or he had done wrong and that this was God's punishment for sin. In the confusion, he was unable to grieve, gave up his beliefs and said that there was no God and that life was pointless.

It has been argued that those who survived best in concentration camps during the Second World War were those who had an inner strength and faith which came from a firm religious or political belief. Bruno Bettelheim (1988) said that Jehovah's Witnesses, who would have been regarded by most psychiatrists as highly neurotic and delusional, showed great human dignity, displayed a high standard of moral behaviour, and survived well because of a kind of aloofness and emotional distancing. He also said that those who survived best were those who retained the ability to choose their own attitudes in any given circumstances.

A story is told of some Jewish Rabbis in a concentration camp who decided to put God on trial. After all the evidence was presented, the conclusion was that God did not exist. One Rabbi then stood up and said that it was time for evening prayers. No matter what happened, belief in God was paramount, even if you could prove that He did not exist!

Clearly, beliefs and attitudes are important in determining how people interpret events and what they do about them, and can influence how they cope and survive. Those who experience trauma and believe that they must get on with their lives and do something positive, such as helping other people, seem to cope better than those who sit and do nothing (Gleser *et al.* 1981). Some develop active, positive coping mechanisms, while others seem to respond with inactivity or passivity, or by avoiding thinking about it or about the consequences or the future. Avoidance can indeed help at the time, but it is not always a successful long-term coping strategy and so should be used only as a temporary measure. Whether avoidance is the result of beliefs or attitudes is not clear, but it does seem to be related to what people have learned, and therefore to character, personality, background and upbringing. The Scott trauma belief inventory lists a series of questions about the kinds of beliefs that do not provide good coping responses to trauma (Scott and Stradling 1992, p. 25 and Appendix C), most of which centre on self-image, self-esteem and trust.

Also, it is possible that those who belong to cohesive and supportive groups, families, churches or other religious or ideological communities may cope better than those who do not. However, this depends to some extent on the nature of any given group's beliefs and on whether the individual concerned accepts such beliefs as supportive.

3 Preparation and support

Training and professionalism
With professional helpers, rescuers and carers, training and experience will to some extent influence beliefs and attitudes. A poorly trained or freshly recruited soldier is not likely to cope well in battle; a novice police officer is usually accompanied by an experienced colleague until he has learned the ropes. Those who are well trained should have developed a strong sense of their own abilities and expertise; in addition, they know that they belong to a supportive and special—even elite—group. During a fire or other disaster there is usually a good support system, comprising senior personnel and other colleagues on hand; provision for rest, hot drinks and food; reliable means of relaying information. Furthermore, the participants may know that when the incident is over their professional organisation will offer sup-

port and help through an Operational Debriefing, as well as any follow-up that may be needed, from any of a number of familiar welfare agencies.

All this normally serves to strengthen the already firm belief in the capabilities both of the individual and of the group, and raises morale. This belief, plus the support of colleagues or comrades, can sustain them and help them to cope. However, it may also mean that defences are stronger and that the determination to cope and survive, come what may, prevails, with the result that, since rescuers expect to rescue and helpers to help, in the event that they can do neither they may feel that they have failed. No matter how competent a doctor, and even when he knows that he has done his best, if someone dies when he is giving medical assistance he may still feel that he has failed. A well trained fire and rescue officer who has saved three lives from a burning building, but not a fourth, may respond in one of two ways:

'I did my best and I am sorry that I couldn't save everyone. But I did save three lives and coped well.'

or:

'I did my best, but I am sorry that I couldn't save everyone. Therefore I have failed. If only we had arrived earlier. If only I had been given better equipment. If only I had run instead of walking. If only . . .'

The first officer has a sense of sadness, but also of achievement and success. The second is racked with guilt and self-blame. Both reactions can be the result of training and experience and of previously held beliefs that a person has about himself and about life. Perhaps the first officer is an optimist and the second a pessimist, and optimists may be more likely to cope than pessimists? In fact, it is impossible to say how even an incurable optimist, who will be expected to have positive attitudes, will react in a given situation. Perhaps the optimist's belief in his professionalism and competence will be severely damaged when he is faced with an event that proves overwhelming? Perhaps the pessimist can never be disappointed and, in some situations, may have a more realistic view? Scheier and Carver (1987) report that optimists have an active and positive problem-solving style which usually produces successful coping strategies and survival mechanisms.

On the whole, professionals cope well with their reactions to traumatic incidents, but many say that the deaths of children and babies are particularly disturbing and difficult to face because they do not make sense.

> John was a police officer, married with two small children, a boy and a girl. He attended a traffic accident where a young child—a boy the same age as his son—had been killed. He coped with the incident and did his job well, but later found that he was identifying the dead child with his own son. He frequently thought of his children, seeing mental pictures of them dead. On a number of occasions he had to get up in the middle of the night and go into their room to check that they were still breathing. He did not suffer from acute trauma, but he had powerful feelings of fear and horror, and the image of the dead boy kept flashing into his mind.

In spite of professionalism and training, such an experience often raises questions about the meaning and purpose of life, and whether it can be seen as fair and just.

Support

In addition to the support given during the incident, it is also important to look at the support given or offered afterwards. Those who belong to unsupportive organisations, groups, families or communities seem likely to cope less well. When American soldiers returned home from Vietnam they found that many despised and rejected them because they felt that they had been engaged in an immoral and unjust war. Even some soldiers felt it. Whatever their feelings, they returned to a land where they were not generally hailed as heroes, but treated as outcasts. Some, unable to cope with this lack of support, left their work and relationships, dropped out of society, even committed suicide.

After traumatic experiences most people need to feel that what they have endured or done is acknowledged, understood and affirmed by others. This can be achieved through an Operational Debriefing immediately after the event, in which the Organisation gathers as a professional group to look at practical aspects of the incident. They are all provided with information and reassurance, and their group solidarity is affirmed. Support can also be offered through defusing and Critical Incident Debriefing. At a simple level, rescue workers and helpers need support in the form of rest, food and drink and an opportunity to talk. Those who are offered such support are likely to cope better than those who are not. This will be discussed in Chapter 4 when we look at treatment.

HOW DO REACTIONS DEVELOP?

Reactions to traumatic events seem to be determined by a number of variables: the nature of the event; the character, personality, previous and present experiences, beliefs, attitudes and expectations of the individual involved; the training, preparation and information that he or she has been given.

A number of different models attempt to relate and explain reactions to these variables.

1 The life-beliefs model
One model for understanding reactions is based on 'life beliefs'. Janoff-Bulman (1985) proposes that throughout our lives, as we grow and develop, we gradually absorb and accept three basic beliefs about ourselves and the world around us. We believe that we are invulnerable, that life has a meaning and a purpose, and that we are reasonably good and respectable people—in other words, we have a good self-image. These beliefs depend on previous experiences inasmuch as the latter have influenced them—which means that some people will be more vulnerable to reactions than others.

Invulnerability

Most people grow up to believe that life is reasonably safe and secure: 'Bad things happen to other people, not to me.' Although we experience various traumas and losses as time goes by, we do not expect to face abnormal traumatic incidents. Being born, learning to separate from mother, going to school for the first time, surviving puberty, leaving school and starting work, being unemployed or made redundant, falling in love, getting married, having children, divorcing, going through the menopause, retiring, growing old and the impending experience of death—all of these are life events, traumatic experiences that can be highly stressful but that we usually accept as 'normal', as part of life.

But we do not expect to be mugged, raped or assaulted, or to be in a car, rail or air crash, or to have our children die. We know that such things are possible, normally accept that they can happen, and then get on with our lives. It is too painful, negative and distressing to think of these things happening to us, so we push the thoughts and feelings away or down inside our minds. At certain times we may be more aware of our own vulnerability: when there is a terrorist threat; when we have been told that we have had or could have a heart attack; when we have, or narrowly miss having, an accident; when someone we know or love is threatened in some way, is seriously ill or dies. But even when we are made aware of our own vulnerability, we usually soon cope with the feelings and emotions and carry on with our lives.

When we experience a traumatic incident we are faced with the fact of our own mortality and the frailty of life. Loving someone is considered by most people to be the deepest and most meaningful experience, but it can be very painful. We face the possibility not only of rejection and hurt, but also of losing the person we love. Attachment to anyone or anything means that we can suffer loss, and when this happens it is traumatic; it reminds us of our vulnerability. Furthermore, we usually believe that we have some measure of control over our own lives. To realise that we are vulnerable is also to lose this feeling of being in charge: someone or something can take it away from us— sometimes, without warning. To lose control can mean that we become confused, frightened, disorientated, angry, aggressive; withdrawn and anxious, or hopeless and depressed. Panic or manic behaviour, or resignation or total inactivity, may ensue.

Meaning and purpose

Most people believe that life has meaning and purpose, even if they cannot say exactly what these are. Meaning and purpose are afforded by a combination of people and things: for instance, family and home, partner and children, work and friends; and hobbies and interests, such as one's car or garden. Some would add religion and belief in a God who gives us value as persons, offers us salvation and gives us meaning by requiring us to live a certain kind of life with an ultimate destiny beyond this world. For others, purpose comes simply through being alive, or by living according to humanistic rules or codes of behaviour, or through wanting to make the world a better place in which to live. Whatever the source of this meaning and purpose, traumatic incidents raise many questions about why we exist and how we should live.

A normal response to any trauma is to ask 'Why?', even when we know that there is no rational or logical answer. Those who experience rape, torture, war or other violence ask questions about human nature, about why people behave like this, how they are able to do such terrible things. They may scream at the universe or ask why God allows such things to happen, but for many there are few satisfying answers. The question 'Why?' is not usually a practical one requiring a scientific answer; it is often a question concerning morality, about right and wrong. Being involved in an earthquake, a war or any other traumatic incident can make people feel that they have no control over what is happening, either to them or around them; that life is capricious, brutal, unpredictable and cruel, or a game in which they are mere pawns. Some will conclude that there is no point or purpose in life and feel confusion, helplessness, hopelessness and utter despair. Some may abandon their beliefs, lose interest in self, reject family, friends or society; and a few will commit suicide.

Self-respect and self-image

> 'I'm a reasonably good person, and if I faced a crisis I would
> do the right thing.'

This is a normal belief: most people think that they are as good
as—certainly no worse than—others, and that if they found themselves in a difficult situation they would do their best to help and
would cope.

In reality many people do just this, but a traumatic incident
may nonetheless leave us uncertain about our own abilities and
lead us to question our self-esteem and self-image. When we
experience trauma we do indeed tend to do our best at the time,
because our coping and defence mechanisms enable us to survive
and carry on. A police officer can attend a horrific incident, do
his duty and cope. But later he may ask questions about his
performance and behaviour—for even when we have done our
best we can still feel that we have failed. This can lead to a
further loss of meaning and purpose and the belief that 'I am
not what I thought I was, and I could and should have done
more.'

> A young man involved in a ferry disaster managed to climb out to
> safety from inside the ship. He was asked to go back into the ship
> to help to rescue others, but could not do it and felt a deep sense of
> shame and guilt. His self-esteem plummeted and he stood for hours
> in the harbour where he lived, staring out to sea. He saw himself as
> a total failure.

> A young building society clerk felt that he should have been able
> to do something to stop the armed robbery that took place at his
> branch, and that he should have protected the female members of
> staff; he was a body-building fanatic with a firm belief in his own
> strength and abilities. A shotgun had been thrust into his face and
> he had been told to hand over the money, which he did. The fact
> that he had been petrified and could do nothing resulted in shame
> and guilt and the feeling that he was useless and 'less than a man'.

The experience of almost any kind of trauma can cause us to question our basic beliefs about life and about ourselves. As we have noted, amongst the many possible reactions are fear of the incident happening again, a sense of isolation and withdrawal, shame and guilt, feelings of helplessness, anger at self and at others, sadness and depression. But there can also be positive reactions. Feeling vulnerable can lead to an increase in compassion and in the ability to empathise with others. Some discover new inner strength, more meaning and purpose in their lives and an increase in self-esteem (see Tedeschi and Calhoun 1995, ch. 3).

2   The human-needs model
Traumatic incidents disrupt our beliefs, expectations and assumptions about life and challenge our basic needs; McCann and Pearlman (1990) liken this challenge to driving a car down an unfamiliar road when you have no map and no control over the steering. They propose that reactions to trauma depend to some extent on which needs are most important to an individual, and they list those that they believe are central to any understanding of why people react in different ways to trauma, and why some needs are stronger in some people than in others. These needs are as follows:

Stability
In order to understand personal experience, we need a stable framework of belief. As mentioned earlier, someone with a firm belief in the goodness and omnipotence of God may feel that this gives meaning to his life. A traumatic event may make him question this belief, resulting either in a deeper faith or in a conviction that God does not exist—or, if he does, that he must be either evil or uncaring. Beliefs other than Christian ones can constitute equally important needs, of course.

Safety and invulnerability

As we saw in relation to Janoff-Bulman's scheme, the need to feel safe and invulnerable is basic to human beings. Experiencing a trauma may result in either feelings of vulnerability or a false increase in self-confidence.

Trust

The need to trust others is a primary one. Trauma can make people feel that nobody is trustworthy, that everyone is fickle, unreliable and selfish.

Self-esteem

Not only do we need to have a good feeling about ourselves and our own worth, we also need to be affirmed and acknowledged by others. Traumatic experience can bring a reduction in self-image and self-esteem.

Independence

Although we usually enjoy being loved, parented and cared for, we also need to feel that we are in charge of our own lives. Growing up means growing away and learning to be independent. Trauma can result in actual or imagined loss of independence, and the attendant conviction that life is capricious, or even mal-evolent. The individual may feel—or, indeed, be—either more or less dependent than she was before.

Power

We have a basic need for power over ourselves and over other people. Trauma can leave us feeling powerless, helpless and at the whim of nature or of other people.

Closeness

The need to be close to other people in relationships through belonging to a family, group or community is important. Trauma can produce feelings of isolation, the sense that nobody under-stands or cares.

*   *   *

Two examples may illustrate the human-needs model. During and after a traumatic incident those for whom it is essential to maintain high self-esteem may find their self-image diminished and may become confused about their own worth. The result may be that they think they have failed, that there is little or no hope, that they have not coped and will not be able to cope in the future. Their self-worth has been severely damaged, or even destroyed. Similarly, someone with a strong need for relationships with others may become either very withdrawn and isolated or more clinging.

McCann and Pearlman suggest that when looking at responses to traumatic events we should acknowledge that the needs of individuals will have developed in different ways, and therefore reactions will differ from one person to the next.

3   The independents-and-cling-ons model

Another, similar, theory is based on a study of how people cope with bereavement and loss, and on the concepts of 'projection' and 'identification' as put forward by Lily Pincus in her book, *Death and the Family* (1976). Pincus recognises two kinds of people: those who are independent and those who cling to others.

Independents

Pincus proposes that individuals with high self-esteem tend to cope better with bereavement and loss than those with low self-esteem. These copers are people who can be described as 'independents'. They do need others, but can cope without them and 'stand on their own two feet'. They are probably people who had a supportive and positive upbringing and felt cared for and loved and, on the strength of this, learned to separate successfully from mother and family. They cope because they believe in themselves. They are able to say, 'Not only am I loved, I am lovable. I am of value.' Having learned to make their own way in the world, when they attach themselves to people or things or to life in general they do not cling. In a marriage or partnership they love no less than others, but tend to have their own separate interests. They do not need to do everything with their partner or wear similar clothes. When bereaved they say, 'Something has been torn from me', and they feel empty inside, but they survive because they have an inner sense of worth that is not dependent on someone or something else. Although they grieve, they can cope without the lost object or person; they remain whole and retain a positive sense of who they are. Their world will not be destroyed by trauma.

Cling-ons

Some people can be described as the 'cling-ons' (my term) in life: they need other people and things in order to be themselves. In early life they probably learned—or came to believe, rightly or wrongly—that they were not really loved and so were of little worth. They were unable to achieve a healthy separation from parents and home; they needed to belong in order to be themselves. In their relationships with, and attitudes to, people or objects, work and the world around them, they need to cling desperately in order to give themselves meaning and purpose— 'Without you, I am nothing.' But this is more than simply clinging; they internalise this 'other', which becomes part of who and what they are and is incorporated into their personal identity— hence Pincus' use of the term 'identification'. They cannot be themselves without it. When they experience loss or bereavement they say, 'Something has died inside me', and this something remains inside, in the way that in some science fiction films an alien creature takes over a human being and lives inside him or her.

The 'independents' have lost something or someone; it has gone away—'Something has been torn from me.' The 'cling-ons', on the other hand, find that the something or someone is still there, dead inside them.

These concepts may be important when looking at how people react to trauma, and why they react as they do. The independents may cope better than the cling-ons. My experience of twenty-five years as a chaplain in the army is that those who cope best with retirement or redundancy are those who do not make the army their whole life's interest. They have a relationship with the army in which it never completely takes over their lives; although inside it, they are able to stand outside and look inwards. Leaving may be difficult, but they are able to move into civilian life and adjust to the new environment. Those who have problems on leaving or retiring may be people who have not only given a total commitment of body and soul to the army, but who have internalised it and cannot let go or cope without it. It became not just a job, but part of their personality and character. It defined who they were, and it defines who they still are.

For one, the independent, the army has gone away; for the other, the cling-on, it is dead inside him. Both can be equally effective and efficient within the army, but one may find it easier to cope with leaving than the other.

It is impossible, nonetheless, to say exactly how either the independents or the cling-ons will react to and cope with trauma. Perhaps the independents will cope better because of the strength of their personality and high self-esteem? Perhaps they will cope less well because any feelings such as anger and isolation, though quite normal given the situation, may be totally unexpected and unfamiliar and result in confusion? The cling-ons may cope by desperately holding on to a belief or idea, no matter how strange or incredible. The religious cling-ons may hold fast to the belief that whatever happens has a purpose or plan, and then devise what they believe to be arguments in support of this idea.

When I served as a clergyman in Liverpool, many local people coped with the deaths of babies and children by saying that it must be all part of God's purpose. But although the basic belief that everything was planned by God might have been acceptable to some, they would also argue that 'God picks only the best flowers first', and 'God took him because he needed him in Heaven.' They would cling to these explanations come what may, and they did indeed help them to cope. As well as seeming to deal with the question of why things happen and permitting them to retain a belief in a God who was good and who had a purpose for his creation, such explanations also gave value to their loss.

A man who was not religious lost most of his immediate family in a tragedy. He believed that he had survived for a purpose, for which he gave two reasons: first, that the others could not have coped with the loss and, second, that he alone was strong enough to help the surviving members of the family. He clung to these beliefs and they helped him to cope, even though he was severely depressed and unable to grieve.

The distinction between those who are independent and those who cling may be useful in determining how and why some people react to trauma but, as with many generalisations, the two concepts are at opposite ends of a wide spectrum, with most people somewhere in between.

4   The marshmallow test

In determining how people react to life and cope with stress and trauma, Daniel Goleman (1996) discusses the difference between 'emotional intelligence' and IQ. In the 1960s the psychologist Walter Mischel, at Stanford University in California, conducted a simple test involving the use of a marshmallow with a large group of four-year-olds from a nursery. Placing a marshmallow in front of each child, he told them that either they could have that marshmallow now, or, if they waited while he went away to deal with something else, on his return they could have two. Three out of four children resisted the temptation and waited until he returned. The others tended to grab the marshmallow right away, seemingly preferring immediate gratification to waiting for a bigger reward. Goleman maintained that this demonstrated the differing abilities of the children to control their reactions and emotions.

This same group of children were tested in their teens, and those who had resisted the tempting marshmallow were shown to be more self-assertive, rather than aggressive, and were better able to cope with social life and with the general frustrations of living. Also, they coped better with stress and remained calm under pressure. They welcomed change and challenge in their lives, and were determined to succeed, whatever happened to them. In character, they were trustworthy, self-reliant, confident and dependable. Those who had grabbed the marshmallow, on the other hand, turned out to have fewer of these positive qualities. They were shy, indecisive, stubborn and easily upset and frustrated when things went wrong. They tended to be envious and jealous and found it difficult to cope with, or adjust to, change and stress. When problems arose they would often lose their temper, lose control or over-react in some other way.

Mischel argued that for four-year-olds the marshmallow test was a better indicator of future achievement and progress than IQ tests. He coined the concept of 'emotional intelligence' (EI); those who scored high in this field, he said, developed qualities that would enable them to cope well in life. The high scorers in the EI tests could regulate their moods, control their behaviour and reactions, and prevent distress from overwhelming their ability to empathise with others or to hope. Other positive qualities of those who had not grabbed the lone marshmallow were self-awareness and the ability to know and manage their own emotions; self-motivation and the ability to curb their impulses; the ability to recognise and empathise with emotions in others; the ability to cope with relationships. Goleman argues that those who score high in emotional intelligence tests tend to cope better with the changes and chances of life; they worry less, tend not to be fearful, can express their feelings more easily; are more assertive, feel positive about themselves and believe in a meaning and purpose in life.

It is possible that those who display these qualities of emotional intelligence are also those who cope best with stress and trauma. Such qualities would develop in the early years of life and continue through puberty, producing adults who possess the ability to cooperate with and listen to others and resolve conflict, as well as all the other attributes listed above.

The life-beliefs, human-needs and projection-and-identification models, and the marshmallow test, are some of the models with which therapists and others are attempting to understand human reactions to traumatic events. What seems to emerge is that those who have, or who are able to develop, positive attitudes to themselves and to life in general are more likely to cope with trauma, stress and change than those who do not.

The ability to cope will be considered further in Chapter 3, and in Chapter 4 when we look at the ideas and research of Donald Meichenbaum and the factors that influence treatment. Meichenbaum (1994) believes that, when traumatised, people do not react in a predictable manner, like automatons, but often develop new ideas and beliefs and new ways of looking at themselves and at the world. Their responses are the result of the need, desire and attempt to interpret and make sense of their experiences—all of which is at the heart of the Critical Incident Debriefing model.

2 Post-traumatic Stress and Post-traumatic Stress Disorder

WHAT IS POST-TRAUMATIC STRESS?

In the USA a useful distinction is made between 'eu-stress' and 'dys-stress'. Eu-stress (using the Greek prefix *eu*, meaning 'good', as in 'euphoria') is the normal stress we experience simply from being alive and breathing. The heart, beating and pumping blood around the body, creates pressure and stress. In addition, we live in a world that is constantly changing. Moving around, working and being in relationships all generate different degrees of stress, but this stress is natural and without it we would not survive or cope. The increase in stress that we experience when driving a car, for instance, usually indicates that we are coping with other drivers and road conditions and will reach our destination safely. Eu-stress is therefore good stress.

This normal stress level varies, and usually we cope, but sometimes it rises to the point where it becomes disturbing. Acute stress produces the 'flight or fight' reaction in which our minds and bodies are prepared either to run away or to stay and fight. The heart beats faster, breathing rate increases, and substances such as glucose and adrenalin are pumped into the system to enable us to react effectively. We are ready to go, all wound up like a spring in a machine. However, in some situations we can neither run away nor fight, and the result is a sharp increase in the level of stress. Eu-stress then becomes 'dys-stress' (from the Greek prefix *dys*, which means 'bad' —as in 'dyspepsia' and 'dysfunction'. As we move from eu-stress into dys-stress we experience physical and emotional tension as well as reactions such as anxiety, panic, anger, irritability and frustration. Initially we may deny that there are any problems, but if the stress level carries on rising we begin to feel angry and guilty, to experience a sense of failure, and we become disillusioned and depressed. If this situation continues, we cease to function effectively and eventually experience what is sometimes called a 'nervous breakdown' or 'burn-out'.

This process of moving into distress can be slow, and normally we break off and stop before we break down. However, some events are sudden and dramatic and involve violence and threat, and are beyond our capacity to cope. Such experiences result in post-traumatic stress (PTS), a condition that can influence an individual's feelings about himself and others and about the world around him. His partner, his children and his colleagues, as well as the individual himself, may be caught up in changes outside their usual experience and beyond their control. The outcome may be ill health, problems at work, marital stress and the breakdown of relationships.

Two main types of stressors result in post-traumatic stress reactions:

1 Natural disasters.
2 Man-made disasters.

1 Natural disasters

These include earthquakes, drought, volcanic eruptions, typhoons, floods, tornadoes and hurricanes. They often affect whole communities, and in some cases entire countries. When natural disasters result in deaths, injuries and the destruction of buildings including homes, there can be feelings of extreme vulnerability and of loss of control over oneself and the environment. Natural disasters—described as 'natural' because they often have no apparent cause other than the unpredictability of nature—disrupt physical and social communications and destroy our usual sense of safety and security.

2 Man-made disasters

These include war, terrorism, genocide, torture, rape, hostage situations, armed robberies, kidnappings—any traumatic experiences where human beings, intentionally or unintentionally, are the cause. Recent examples in the UK are:

- The *Herald of Free Enterprise* ferry off Zeebrugge on 6 March 1987: 193 people were killed.
- The King's Cross Fire in London on 18 November 1987: 31 died.
- The bombing of the Pan Am jumbo jet over Lockerbie on 21 December 1988: 259 died.
- The Boeing 737 Kegworth air crash beside the M1 on 8 January 1989: 47 were killed.
- The Hillsborough football stadium disaster on 15 April 1989: 95 died.
- The *Marchioness* boat disaster on the Thames on 20 August 1989: 51 died.

Man-made disasters usually involve intense feelings of terror, horror and helplessness. They disrupt and overturn our normal beliefs and expectations, and produce feelings of acute vulnerability. They can result in the conviction that life is without meaning and purpose and destroy our feelings of innate goodness and self-esteem.

This division of traumatic events into natural and man-made is based on causes, but they can also be categorised according to *how* they occur. They can be sudden, unexpected and short-lived (Type 1), or last a long time (Type 2); and such factors tend to generate different reactions.

Type 1: Sudden
One-off events that happen without any warning and are usually devastating. They include car and aeroplane crashes, rape, robbery, assault—in fact, any experience of sudden violence or trauma. Usually short-lived and dramatic, they disturb the individual's stability and can become indelibly printed on the

memory. Such memories can be intrusive, and difficult to cope with and to treat. Symptoms of arousal, or increased sensitivity (see page 44), are particularly common.

Type 2: Prolonged

These are experiences that occur over a long period, or that happen over and over again. They result in feelings of helplessness and the belief that such events are inevitable. Some man-made disasters fall into this category, including combat stress, terrorism, torture, hostage situations, poverty and hunger. The reactions of those involved may be dissociation and detachment from life, and suppression of painful memories; self-destructive behaviour; feelings of uselessness and loss of control; feelings of failure and despair; sadness or depression; the loss of previously held beliefs; social isolation and withdrawal; personality change; problems with relationships. Possible other effects are claustrophobia, agoraphobia, drug abuse, panic attacks and obsessive–compulsive behaviour. Some begin to believe that nobody cares—then, when people do show that they care, the existing feelings of guilt and inadequacy may be reinforced and intensified.

However they occur, traumatic events can severely disrupt the lives of both victims and helpers.

DEFINING POST-TRAUMATIC STRESS

Post-traumatic stress can be defined as the 'normal reaction of normal people to abnormal events'—a definition that may be unhelpful to sufferers because their reactions often do not feel normal. Another commonly used definition is:

> The development of characteristic symptoms following a psychologically distressing event which is outside the range of normal human experience.

This definition raises a number of questions:

1 Which 'characteristic symptoms'?
2 What is a 'psychologically distressing event'?
3 What is 'normal'?

1 Characteristic symptoms

The 'characteristic symptoms' of post-traumatic stress are diverse and complex and, as we have already noted, different people react to incidents in different ways. Furthermore, the list of reactions is constantly expanding, as researchers, therapists, psychiatrists and others are identifying more and more 'characteristic symptoms': if it is decided that 'Gulf War syndrome', for instance, is indeed due to the traumatic stress of combat, then further symptoms will need to be added to the list. Research suggests that the typical post-traumatic stress disorder reactions of re-experiencing, avoidance behaviour and arousal—also typical of PTS—are rarely found alone but are usually combined with depression, anxiety states, drug abuse or psychosomatic disorders (Green 1994). There are also many symptoms that are similar to bereavement and loss reactions (these PTS and PTSD reactions will be considered in more detail later).

The word 'symptoms' usually suggests an illness with a specific cause followed by specific reactions. The exact causes of traumatic symptoms, which can be anything from mild and temporary to persistent, disabling and extreme, are as yet unknown. It is generally accepted that traumatic reactions are symptomatic not of physical or mental illness or weakness, but of extreme stress. Unless there are physical injuries, those who experience PTS are not in need of medical attention. However, if reactions are distressing enough or fit into the criteria for PTSD, treatment is normally given by a psychiatrist, psychologist, therapist or counsellor. Because we are not dealing here with a finite set of specific indicators, it seems more appropriate to refer to responses as 'reactions' rather than 'symptoms'. These reactions span a wide spectrum of possibilities, from none or short-lived at one end, to acute, delayed, intermittent or chronic at the other. Some people appear not to be affected at all (Quarantelli 1985); some feel little or nothing at the time, but experience reactions when the incident is over; others experience reactions at the time, manage to control or suppress them and then re-experience them years later.

2   A psychologically distressing event

It would be helpful to add the word 'perceived' to all definitions of PTS and PTSD, because reactions will almost certainly reflect the way the event is interpreted by the person involved in terms of their previous and present life experiences. PTS reactions can develop from incidents which some would not see as life-threatening or traumatic and in which neither fear nor helplessness is evident. It has already been emphasised that what is psychologically distressing for one person may not be for another. Many events *may* be traumatic: for instance, divorce, discovering that you were adopted, being given bad news; being unemployed or made redundant, or retirement; bereavement, losing a limb or one's sight, the suicide or murder of a friend, colleague or family member; abortion, sexual abuse, being burgled. But any definition of what is considered to be psychologically distressing needs to take into account the way a particular person interprets their experience and reacts to it.

3   Outside the range of normal human experience

Any experience that one person thinks is 'normal' another may find 'abnormal'. As with what is 'psychologically distressing', this raises the problem of what is normal. If, unlike all my friends and family, I have not been divorced, I may consider myself to be abnormal. Then, if it happens to me as well I may see myself as normal—but, on the other hand, I may still think myself abnormal because, at present, only two out of five marriages end this way. Whether seen as normal or not, the experience of divorce can certainly be traumatic. Furthermore, even an event that is experienced as normal by the individual concerned may still result in PTS reactions. For example, it is normal for a soldier to experience combat and his training should help him to cope. However, killing people, seeing comrades killed and experiencing the terror and horror of war can generate many different reactions—from apathy, lack of concern and numbness, to fear, regret and guilt. The soldier may cope at the time, then later develop PTS reactions and PTSD. Here we move into the already mentioned variables of event, personality, character, beliefs, needs, previous experiences, training and support which must all be taken into account when trying to decide what is normal in human experience; these will be considered further in Chapter 4.

CHARACTERISTICS OF POST-TRAUMATIC STRESS

In any situation where loss or intense stress is the salient factor, a wide range of reactions may be found. These reactions can be categorised into feelings, behaviour and physical effects; and in addition, there is simple denial.

Denial
Usually serving as a defence mechanism, this is a powerful reaction, especially in men, and may prevent them from seeking help. The simple question, 'How are you?', will often elicit the reply, 'I'm all right thank you. I can cope.' Similarly, to the question 'Do you need any help?', the answer will almost always be 'No thank you, I'm OK', especially from professional rescuers and helpers.

Feelings
- Sense of pointlessness—'Why bother? Why go on?'
- Increased anxiety and feelings of vulnerability.
- Depression or sadness.
- Intrusive thoughts and images.
- Fear, shame, anger, regret, guilt or bitterness.
- Survivor guilt—'Why did I survive when they didn't? I should have died instead of them.'
- Sense of isolation—'Nobody understands, even those who were with me.'
- Belief that a heart attack is imminent.
- Strong feelings of group identity with other victims—'The

only people I can relate to are those who were with me.'
- Fear of closed or open spaces.
- Fear of crowds or groups of people.
- Fear of being in the same position—'It can happen again.'
- Sympathy for the aggressors—'the Stockholm syndrome'— resulting from being a prisoner, as in hostage situations.
- Inability to feel anything other than numbness.
- Loss of confidence, low self-esteem and feelings of use- lessness.

Behaviour

- Inability to concentrate or make even simple decisions.
- Impulsive actions—excessive spending, moving home, changing job or lifestyle, ending or creating new relationships.
- Irritability, anger or violence.
- Sleep disturbances—dreams and nightmares.
- Inability to sleep.
- Retreat into isolation—hiding away.
- Incessantly talking about the event—keeping a diary about it.
- Refusal to talk about the event.
- Manic or obsessive–compulsive behaviour.
- Excitement or hyperactivity.
- Inability or unwillingness to do anything—e.g., not wanting to get out of bed in the morning.

Physical effects

- Non-specific ailments—headaches, stomach pains, tightness in the chest, feeling generally unwell, dyspepsia, sweating, palpitations, increased heart rate and blood pressure, dry mouth, tension.
- Listlessness and constant exhaustion.
- Excitement, arousal, hyperactivity; inability to sit still or con- centrate.
- Increased smoking or drinking; and, possibly, the use of drugs, usually to dull the senses and create a sense of euphoria.

- Loss of mechanical skills.

Moreover, changes in values or beliefs and readjustments in relationships may be evident, in comments such as: 'What's the point of marriage, work or relationships or of living when something like this has happened?' Some will discover a new faith, and some will lose faith; others may find that already held beliefs, ideas or attitudes are consolidated.

The loss of personal possessions or of homes or other buildings, or the destruction of familiar landmarks, can have similar effects, causing confusion, disorientation and anger. This happened after an earthquake in Mexico where the centre of a town was destroyed. The buildings symbolised something about the community—they had given a sense of pride, security and belonging. Detachment from previous relationships and way of life, or a new clinging and sense of dependency, are yet other possible responses to trauma.

There can also be positive reactions, such as an enhanced feeling of the worthwhileness of life and of relationships, and a sense of achievement.

CHARACTERISTICS OF POST-TRAUMATIC STRESS DISORDER

The criteria for the diagnosis of post-traumatic stress disorder are laid down in the *Diagnostic and Statistical Manual of Mental Disorders* (*DSM*) of the American Psychiatric Association (the most recent edition is the revised manual of 1994, *DSM IV*). The main reactions in PTSD are re-experiencing the event, avoidance behaviour and arousal.

Re-experiencing the event
These experiences are also called 'flash-backs', because the individual finds himself inadvertently flashing back to the event. Some or all of the reactions, feelings and emotions associated with the event are as real as if they were happening all over again in the present. Flash-backs can occur soon after the incident, or days, months or even years later; one ex-prisoner of war described

it as 'accessing the memory banks'. Such reactions can either be triggered by external events, or emerge 'out of the blue'.

Triggered reactions

● *Sights*   TV programmes or images, videos, photographs, media reports, people—in fact, anything visual—can remind the individual of the incident. A war film can result in painful memories for someone who has been in combat; a television report about a car crash can trigger feelings for someone who has experienced a traffic accident. Feelings such as panic, anger, distress, guilt, fear and horror, experienced earlier, can come flooding back.

> The reactions of a man who had been in a traffic accident were triggered by the sight of a particular colour and make of car: he instantly heard the sound of a police siren and could smell burning rubber and petrol.

● *Sounds*   Police, ambulance and fire and rescue sirens, bangs, crashes, voices, accents—anything heard at the time of the incident—may cause flash-backs.

> A young man who had been involved in a shooting in which he saw others shot dead and thought that he too was going to die jumped violently and began to panic when a balloon burst at a children's party.

> A veteran of the Falklands War dropped to the ground in the High Street of his home town when a car backfired. He had felt he was back in combat and that someone was shooting at him.

● *Smells*   Petrol, rubber, disinfectant, water, dampness, sweat, food, flowers, animals, breath—the smell of anything that was encountered during the event—can evoke a reaction.

> A young woman who faced the raider in an armed robbery threw

away her husband's after-shave because the smell reminded her of the smell of the robber.

- *Tastes* The taste of food, water, petrol, alcohol, sweat, or even having a dry mouth, can bring back feelings and emotions.

- *The feel of things* The feel of rubber, plastic, hot metal, skin or water, for example, or being touched or held in any particular place or way, can cause re-experiencing. Someone who has been in a car crash may begin to panic when sitting behind a steering-wheel for the first time since the incident.

> A young man driving a car had an accident in which his friend, who was sitting in the back, was killed. When he was eventually able to sit in the driving seat of a car again he saw his friend, through the rear-view mirror, sitting on the back seat. This caused intense fear and panic.

All of these triggers can result in emotions and feelings from the past intruding into the present.

'Out of the blue' reactions
These reactions, too, occur at any time and without any warning—for instance, at home, at work, in the street, while shopping or resting. And, because they have no apparent trigger, they can be even more frightening or overwhelming.

> A prison officer who had been involved in a riot found himself, a few days later, sitting on the floor of a supermarket completely disorientated and in a state of bewilderment. Feelings that he had experienced during the riot suddenly came rushing into the present. Although he was not aware of it at the time, he thought later that this could have been brought on by the crowds and noise of the supermarket.

Such experiences, which are probably the result of hidden, suppressed or repressed feelings and sensations coming to the surface, are common after trauma.

Avoidance behaviour
Those who have been involved in a traumatic event may seek to
avoid anything or anyone that might remind them of the incident:
for instance, flying, or getting on to a horse or a ferry, or into a
car; reunions, anniversaries or birthdays; colleagues, family or
friends; open spaces, trees, certain rooms or places. Some try to
avoid certain thoughts, feelings or situations because they bring
back painful memories; others are unable to recall any feelings
or to remember what happened. There can be loss of concentration; loss of acquired skills; feelings of isolation and loneliness,
of numbness and emptiness. Individuals may feel hopeless, and
unable to have or express feelings of love and affection towards
family and friends. Some will avoid thinking about the future,
may not expect to live long, and may feel a sense of doom.

Arousal
Increased sensitivity to noise, even to the slightest sound, can
cause people to jump nervously in an exaggerated startle
response. This may indicate an inability to accept the usual stress
of work, home or family life. Children playing or a friend or
partner talking can lead to outbursts of anger, or even violence,
and some retreat into isolation.

> A married soldier, a veteran of the Falklands War, would lock himself
> in a room for long periods and then emerge and become abusive
> and violent towards his wife and children.

This increased arousal can result in sleeplessness or difficulty
in concentration; some become hypervigilant, always expecting
the worst to happen, at any time and without warning. A person
walking down the street may believe that 'something dreadful is
going to happen when I reach the next corner'. When it does not
happen, far from being relieved, he thinks that it will happen
when he gets to the corner after that. Or something out of place
at home, such as a piece of furniture, can cause intense, irrational
anger and the conviction that it has been moved deliberately or
out of lack of regard for the person concerned. Reactions like

these are often exaggerations of normal feelings. Instead of feeling slightly annoyed about the thoughtless behaviour of another
driver or of a waiter in a restaurant, the individual's reactions
can escalate to extreme anger or violence. Some direct their
aggression and emotions at the organisations or institutions that
they consider responsible for what has happened; others feel the
desire to take revenge.

> A Falklands War veteran suffering from PTSD experienced bouts
> of extreme anger and wanted to burn down Ministry of Defence
> buildings because he believed that he had been treated badly by the
> military.

In short, the world is seen as a dangerous and unjust place
where nobody can be trusted.

Behaviour caused by increased arousal sometimes appears to
help at the time, but more often it results in further anger, guilt,
regret, bitterness and despair.

> 'I feel better for expressing my anger, but it does not help my
> marriage because it hurts my wife and children. It also proves
> just how hopeless and useless I am.'

Some seem to be able to cope only in situations of high drama.
Having experienced a traumatic incident, they cannot deal with
what they now perceive to be the boring and mundane things in
life.

> A soldier who had served in Bosnia where he lived in almost constant
> fear of being shot or killed, coped by suppressing his feelings and
> by drinking alcohol. After living in this highly charged atmosphere
> he returned home to his family in England, where he found it difficult
> to adjust and to adapt his newly acquired ways of reacting and coping
> to such a very different situation. He isolated himself from his family
> by aggressive behaviour and further drinking.

> A soldier who had served in Northern Ireland was made redundant;
> when he began to experience PTSD reactions he described civilian

life as 'trivial' and civilians as 'shallow'. He now had nobody to fight, he said, and felt that everything was meaningless and that ideas of civilised behaviour no longer seemed to matter. His wife commented, 'He can't express any feelings of affection and it seems that he doesn't care, but we know that deep down he does care.'

These three reactions—re-experiencing, avoidance behaviour and arousal—are often linked together in a vicious circle.

'I am frightened of re-experiencing emotions, feelings and thoughts, so I try to avoid anything that might make this happen. In trying to avoid feelings and thoughts I suppress them, but they have a habit of coming to the surface and, as a result, I become aroused. The more I try to avoid them, the more tense I feel and the more I am in danger of re-experiencing them. Then, when I do re-experience them, the more destructive they are and the more angry I become. I then try even harder to repress them, and the cycle begins all over again. These reactions seem to lurk in the depths of my mind like a great monster waiting to be released. But the monster just lies there and seems to destroy me, and I have no control over what happens and how I react.'

DIAGNOSING PTSD

The *Diagnostic and Statistical Manual of Mental Disorders IV* (1994) gives the following list of criteria for diagnosing PTSD.

There must have been exposure to a traumatic event which entailed:

- *Threat of injury or death*   Experiencing, witnessing or being confronted by an event which results in actual or threatened death, or serious injury or threat to the physical integrity of the self or of others.
- *Fear, helplessness or horror*   In children, intense fear, help-

lessness or horror may be expressed through behaviour and play rather than verbally.

There must also be the following symptoms:

- Re-experiencing of reactions, feelings and emotions associated with the incident.
- Persistent avoidance behaviour and numbing of responses.
- Persistent symptoms of arousal.

In addition:

- The symptoms should have persisted for more than a month.
- The symptoms should cause significant distress and impairment of functions in the individual, with family or with friends, and at work.

Symptoms are:

- *Acute* if they persist for less than three months after the incident.
- *Chronic* if they persist for more than three months after the incident.
- *Delayed* or intermittent when they occur later.

Despite the devastating effects that PTSD can wreak upon individuals, groups and families, human beings have a remarkable capacity to survive, adapt and cope. This is the subject of the next chapter.

3   Coping Strategies

Most people, especially professionals such as police, fire and rescue and ambulance officers, soldiers, doctors and nurses, cope very well with traumatic incidents, and if they do develop distressing reactions they normally recover after a short while. They cope, both during and after incidents, by using various strategies, some of which are natural reactions; others have been learned from previous experience and during training. Some of the strategies used are deliberate attempts to suppress reactions, and others are unconscious.

BEFORE THE INCIDENT

It is important that those who conduct Debriefing sessions be aware of the *defence mechanisms* of denial and distancing.

Denial

The normal reaction to the shock of a traumatic incident is usually the powerful defence of denial.

> 'It hasn't affected me in any way at all.' 'It's just a job and somebody has to do it.' 'I'm all right. I don't need any help.'

Telling someone that a relative has died often elicits the reply, 'It can't be true, I was talking to her only last night.' This is a common reaction to any experience of loss—we cannot believe that things like this happen, so we deny it. It can happen, for instance, when you are told that you have, or someone you love has, cancer, or must have an operation; that you are to be made redundant; that your partner is going to divorce you. Similarly, people sometimes have no conscious recollection of having been given the news that they are terminally ill. Denial is switched on as a protection against the unacceptable, both during and after an incident. Whether conscious or unconscious, it helps us to maintain control and to survive.

Distancing

Many use a process called 'distancing', which attempts to remove them from what they are doing, seeing and feeling. It is achieved through use of the following strategies, some of which derive from a research paper presented by Dyregrov and Mitchell (1992) relating to a bus crash in Norway in August 1988 in which twelve children and three adults were killed. Some of these strategies are also used by social workers mentioned in a report on stress in social work teams in a Social Services department (Parkinson 1992). Each of the percentages given below represents the number of rescue workers who said they used the strategy in question (as recorded by Dyregrov and Mitchell).

Keeping busy *94%*

When things go wrong, one of our oldest strategies is to 'do something'. Doing something means that our minds are diverted from what has just happened; doing something can give us the impression that we are not useless, that we are exerting some element of control. When involved in a traumatic incident, we may well just concentrate on what we were already doing, ignore what is happening around us and avoid absorbing information related to the incident. This is similar to the strategy for coping with stress that involves taking exercise, being active: for instance, jogging, cycling, swimming or running. In traumatic incidents, keeping busy and focusing on a specific task can help to take our minds off the horror or tragedy in which we find ourselves suddenly involved. It can enable us to exclude the implications of what is happening.

Giving mutual support   *90%*

During traumatic incidents rescuers and helpers are not usually
on their own, but surrounded by colleagues and by others from
different organisations. There is usually much talking and touching between teams and groups, which gives both emotional and
physical support and helps to maintain morale and feelings of
solidarity.

> Following an accident, one man reported that a simple tap on the
> shoulder from a doctor had given him great encouragement.

The knowledge that others are there with you can give comfort
and strength. It also encourages the belief that 'if they can cope,
so can I'.

Suppressing and repressing emotions   *76%*

Many make a conscious effort to control and suppress any reactions, by the use of emotional detachment. During the incident
they prevent adverse or unhelpful reactions or feelings from
emerging. This strategy is useful and necessary, especially for
professionals. It would not be helpful for a police or fire and
rescue officer to break down and cry, to start screaming or to
run away when the aim is to rescue people and save lives. Furthermore, this *suppression* of emotions can continue long after the
event, and may lead to feelings being *repressed*—that is, pushed
deeper inside. We can usually access suppressed feelings, but we
may well believe that repressed emotions and memories have
gone away for good. Useful as this strategy can be at the time,
such emotions and feelings may emerge later, especially when
triggered by external events; or they may happen without warning
as flash-backs, typical of PTS and PTSD reactions.

Maintaining a sense of unreality 68%

With any traumatic incident there is the initial experience of shock, which can numb reactions and make the incident seem unreal. Afterwards, some will say that they felt as though they were acting in a film or play, but that this helped them to cope. Others recall the feeling of floating outside themselves as in an 'out-of-body experience', or watching themselves from afar or on a video.

Avoiding disturbing thoughts 68%

Some feel emotionally detached. To them, the bodies of the dead or injured seem like dummies in an exercise. Some even consciously think that the dead are not real human beings. This strategy tends not to work for very long, because feelings often intrude and come to the surface.

> In one incident in Bosnia, involving the burnt bodies of murdered men, women and children, the soldiers who were given the gruesome task of moving the bodies coped by giving them marks out of ten for the degree of burntness. This helped them to avoid thinking of the bodies as real people. To do otherwise would have been too painful, and they probably would not have coped. But when it was over, many of them broke down and cried.

Preparing mentally 63%

Some believe that mental and emotional preparation before the incident helps—not just professional preparation, but thinking of the information given about the incident and comparing it with previous or similar ones: 'If I have coped with a similar event in the past, I will cope again.' This does not always help, though. With the bus crash in Norway, for instance (Dyregrov and Mitchell 1992), the rescuers probably expected to find mainly middle-aged or elderly victims. They were shocked and stunned to discover dead children. Making comparisons with previous traumatic incidents is not helpful if the event turns out to be very different in important respects.

Being professionally trained 48%

Almost half of those surveyed by Dyregrov and Mitchell felt that being professionally trained for the task helped. Knowing what to do, previous experience and professional team solidarity resulted in trust and confidence in both self and in colleagues. For bystanders, witnesses and non-professional helpers the experience of an accident or disaster can be so overwhelming that they themselves become victims.

Regulating exposure 38%

Limiting the amount of time when they are actively involved prevents people from becoming exhausted and ineffective and from making wrong decisions. But rest periods should not last too long, or they may begin to 'switch off' and find that conflict is caused by their using coping strategies when working and then not having to use them when resting. Dyregrov and Mitchell found that some sought out information, while others avoided learning anything about what was happening elsewhere at the scene. Those who did not want information felt that not knowing helped, in that they were able to concentrate on the task in hand. In addition, the pressure and desire to continue in order to save lives makes some feel that they should not have any breaks at all.

Having a sense of purpose 20%

The feeling that 'I have to do it and I am the right person to do it' is not uncommon. Knowing that you are helping can be important: 'I am doing it for this person or for his relatives.' This strategy was used by many who belonged to the Graves' Registration Team during the Gulf War. They felt that it was a difficult and distressing job but that they had been trained to do it, and were doing it for the individuals who had been killed and for their families. This gave them a sense of purpose.

Keeping their minds off it 20%

While working at the scene of an incident some think of their homes or gardens, of what meals they will be having or what they may be doing that evening, the next day or next week. Some will sing or talk to themselves in order to create a reality outside the incident and to take their minds off what they are doing.

Humour 16%

Humour can be a positive way of coping with trauma. It is used among those belonging to the same professional group—police, fire and rescue workers, medical staff, clergy and others—but not, generally, when 'outsiders', such as survivors, relatives or onlookers, are present. When children are involved, humour does not feature prominently, as the percentage above (relating to the Norwegian bus crash) indicates. Alexander and Wells (1990) report that 98 per cent of police officers who worked in the mortuary after the Piper Alpha oil-rig disaster found the use of humour helpful. According to Hetherington and Guppy (1990), police traffic officers said that humour is useful when attending accidents. In child-care teams dealing with abused children, the butts of their humour—often very 'black', or 'sick'—were the abusers, not the victims. Humour is a way of releasing emotions, but also of avoiding or hiding feelings. It can offer a temporary release from the serious or horrifying effects of the incident on the individual or group, but it is not a strategy that should be used for any length of time. It can suppress real feelings, leading to the possibly mistaken belief that people are coping. But those real feelings, if suppressed or repressed in this way, can emerge later—sometimes with devastating effect.

AFTER THE INCIDENT

People use various coping strategies *after* traumatic incidents, including some of those mentioned above, such as continuing to avoid feelings by means of black humour and by suppressing emotions. The following are commonly employed by social workers (Parkinson 1992), and by other professionals.

Talking to themselves, or to a colleague, friend or partner
Some said that they talked to themselves on the way home, or shared feelings and experiences with their partners, colleagues or friends. Some talked to their dog or cat, and others to a photograph of a significant person. However, some said that they could not talk to anyone and just wanted to be left alone; sometimes the rationale was: 'I don't want to burden them further. They have sufficient worries of their own.' Most said that talking did help because they were able to express feelings.

Listening to music
Listening to the radio or to music—sometimes in the car on the way home, or with a personal stereo—helped some people to relax and took their minds off what they had been doing. Personal stereos tend to create an isolated world for the listener, providing a block to both inner thoughts and the outer world. They can be relaxing or invigorating or pleasurable, and offer a safe environment in which to experience emotions and feelings of sadness or sorrow.

Being grateful
Some said that it was helpful to tell themselves that they should be grateful to be alive or to have partners, families, children of their own. Some working in child-abuse teams felt a personal identity with the victims: glad that they themselves were not the victims, they said, 'It could have been me or my child.' This sense of gratitude can sometimes be confused with or lead to feelings of guilt, especially survivor guilt.

Pursuing hobbies, exercise or sport
Those who took exercise or were involved in a sport or hobby felt that this helped. A few were unable to relax, experiencing bouts of anxiety and restlessness, and found great difficulty in sleeping. Those who were unable to concentrate, except for short periods, discovered that this affected their ability to pursue hobbies or to read.

Expressing emotions and feelings
Some were able to express their feelings and emotions afterwards, but others could not. Swearing, clenching the fists, shouting, stamping the feet and banging or throwing things around were all common. On the way home in the car they would scream and shout abuse, at no one in particular; this was helpful, they said, although it was embarrassing when other motorists wondered what they were doing. Others, not wanting to show emotions or feelings in front of colleagues, families or friends, bottled them up inside. Anger was often directed at the employer organisation: those in charge, the supervisors and senior managers, they claimed, just did not care. One sentiment commonly expressed by the social workers was:

> 'Those up there don't care about us down here at the coalface. They are too busy looking upwards to think about us.'

Wanting to be on their own
A few said that they wished to be on their own but, although this seemed to help, it sometimes resulted in feelings of isolation and loneliness. But it was no different for those who had partners and families to whom they opened up: expressing feelings such as anger, guilt and bitterness could result in partners, children or friends withdrawing, thus causing further isolation. Amongst those social workers surveyed, a minority were divorced or separated and lived on their own, and seemed to prefer isolation.

56 Critical Incident Debriefing

Using alcohol and drugs

While recognising that the relief afforded was only temporary, some found that alcohol and drugs helped to suppress the memories and feelings associated with the incident. But because this was seen as a means of avoiding emotions and reactions, or as a sign of weakness, it could lead to depression and guilt.

THE REACTIONS OF HELPERS

Helpers and rescuers, as well as immediate victims, describe feeling a number of reactions both at the time of an incident and later. Dyregrov and Mitchell (1992) report the following:

Negative reactions

Feelings of helplessness
Helpers, rescuers, social workers, doctors, clergy and other professionals expect to be in control and to be able to do something; when they find that they can't, or that they can do very little, they may feel redundant, useless, helpless or impotent.

'I should be able to do something.' 'I should have been able to prevent this.' 'I should have been able to do more.'

Fear and anxiety
Some identify strongly with their own families.

'It could happen to me or my family.' 'I could have been dead.' 'My wife could have been a widow now and my children fatherless.'

There can be acute anxiety: some, for example, will check on their own children by regularly looking into their bedrooms to make sure they are still breathing; others experience sleeplessness, other sleep disturbances, dreams or nightmares, or wake up in the middle of the night in a sweat worrying about what they could, might, or should have done. Some feel such a sense of isolation that they do not want any social contacts outside work, preferring to be alone; others are so exhausted that they just want to sleep.

A *sense of injustice*

Dyregrov and Mitchell call this response 'existential insecurity'. Most people believe that life should be governed by rules of fairness and justice. Traumatic incidents, especially involving the deaths of children, raise questions about the meaning and purpose not only of the incident, but of life itself—'How can such things be allowed to happen?' When children are the victims, deep feelings of injustice are often aroused, and our expectations and beliefs are turned upside down—'Children shouldn't die. Only old people die.' McCammon *et al.* (1988) show that an important coping strategy amongst rescue workers and helpers is the search for meaning and purpose; but the more tragic and distressing the incident, the more difficult it is to do this. Sometimes, the desire for financial compensation on the part of survivors' and victims' families is partly a response to feelings of injustice.

Rage and intolerance

Feelings of rage or anger are often directed at those who are considered responsible for the incident. The desire or need to blame someone or something may also be directed at colleagues, the employer organisation or at oneself. Some people become less tolerant of others' problems, which they see as trivial by comparison, and avoid those whom they perceive as complainers.

> A man involved in a violent riot lost his temper when, on arriving home, he was asked by his wife if he wanted fish fingers and chips or beefburgers and chips. This seemed inconsequential when compared with what he had experienced and was now feeling.

Sorrow and grief

Distress, including crying, is often experienced as a natural reaction when people experience the feelings mentioned above. Men may find it more difficult to cry than women, perhaps because of social conditioning and expectations or the prevalent macho image. People who do not express their feelings at the time may be seen as tough, as copers, but some of those who manage to hide their feelings may say that they feel dreadful inside. Individuals who do express their feelings openly sometimes feel guilty or believe that their partners, families or colleagues will see them as weak and unable to cope.

Intrusive thoughts and images

Intrusive thoughts and images, sometimes triggered by sights, sounds, smells, photographs or TV and other media, are common. These are part of the process of re-experiencing, and are familiar responses to post-traumatic stress. Such thoughts or images can release any of the reactions mentioned above. Some people have images, thoughts and dreams in which they attempt to rearrange what has happened and to change the outcome.

> A young woman who lost relatives in the Zeebrugge incident had thoughts and dreams in which she tried to change the sequence of events so that her family survived.

Self-reproach, shame and guilt

Even when they have done their best during an incident, some ask many questions about themselves and their involvement and performance.

> 'Did I do enough?' 'Did I do what was right?' 'Could I or should I have done more, or done it differently?' 'Did I do my best?' 'If only I had arrived earlier . . .'

This can signal feelings of self-reproach, shame and guilt, and provoke questions about why these things happen. It can also lead to a desire to punish oneself or others, often in a vague attempt to right the wrong.

After the Bradford football stadium fire, one young man felt such shame and guilt at having survived that he was totally unable to ask for help, and wanted to die.

When children are involved, rescue workers and helpers may sometimes increase their normal levels of commitment and personal involvement to the extent that they neglect their own welfare, continuing to work even when they are exhausted. Dyregrov and Mitchell say that emergency workers can often function well at the scene of a disaster until they come across an injured or dead child, or even a child's toy, at which point they may begin to operate less well or break down.

Positive reactions

Not all responses to traumatic incidents are negative. Dyregrov and Mitchell (1992) report the following reactions among rescuers a year after the bus crash involving children:

A deeper appreciation of life
Some felt more strongly than previously that it was good to be alive, that life held much more meaning and purpose. The world seemed a better place in which to live.

A deeper appreciation of others
Some felt that they valued their loved ones more than before, especially their children.

A sense of achievement
Some felt that their own inner resources and strengths had been increased and that they had developed more confidence in themselves and in others. There was a real sense of achievement at what they had done, and they used the word 'awe' to describe how they felt.

The problem was that these positive responses were shown by less than half of those surveyed in the report. The reactions of the rest are not clear, but more than half either did not have positive reactions or were not prepared to say how they had been affected. Tedeschi and Calhoun (1995) in their book *Trauma and Transformation* discuss the ways in which people can grow after traumatic experiences.

WHO COPES BEST?

All the strategies mentioned above help some people to cope and to survive traumatic events, but, as we so often see, different strategies help different people at different times and in different ways. Indeed, what one person finds useful, either at the time or later, may even make matters worse for another.

Most important of all, the strategies of *distancing* and *denial* help professionals to carry out their work and to save lives. However, although especially valuable as part of the package of learned coping mechanisms that can be called upon when needed, they can be destructive if used continually. As already noted, 'black' or 'sick' humour can help to suppress reactions, but used as a long-term strategy it prevents real feelings and emotions from emerging and being dealt with. During the fiftieth anniversary of the Second World War, many ex-service personnel found that extremely distressing feelings, memories and emotions that had been buried were resurrected, and some are now seeking help through counselling and therapy.

Research by Meichenbaum (1994) suggests that those with firm beliefs or who develop particular ways of evaluating a traumatic experience and their own involvement in it tend to cope better than those who do not. Having looked at various literature and research on the subject of coping, Meichenbaum concluded that the following were characteristic of those who seemed to cope best:

- Being able to share problems with others.
- Being able to compare oneself with those less fortunate, and to focus on positive attributes of the experience.
- Being able to learn from the experience.

- Being able to find meaning and purpose in the incident and in one's involvement.
- Being able to compare favourably life now with what it was, and to feel a sense of achievement.
- Being able to find acceptable answers to 'Why?' questions or, in some cases, to stop asking such questions, because there *are* no answers.
- Not feeling personally responsible for what happened.
- Being able to reframe or restructure the incident—which is partly the ability to make some kind of cognitive sense of it and to sort out any resulting confusion.
- Not living out the trauma of the story and experience in one's own life, but seeing it merely as an incident in which one was once involved.
- Being able to place reactions where they belong—that is, in the incident which caused them, rather than in oneself or in one's own abilities or perceived lack of them.

With all of these characteristics, the potential problem lies in the words, 'being able to'; it is not clear what enables some people to take such positive attitudes, but an attempt is made here to explain it in terms of the kind of personality that copes best.

THE SUCCESSFUL COPING PERSONALITY

Tedeschi and Calhoun (1995) outline a number of personality traits that seem to result in the ability to cope better with traumatic experiences. They base their findings on the work of Rotter (1966) in the field of social learning theory. The theory is that, in relation to coping with trauma, those who centre on themselves, on what is called their 'locus of control', rather than on outside influences, cope better with change, stress and trauma than those who focus on others or who look outside themselves for influences on, or causes of, events. Tedeschi and Calhoun record a number of researchers who report that those who cope best are likely to

have the following characteristics (which are similar to those recorded by Meichenbaum (1994)):

- Belief in themselves and in their ability to cope with and face up to challenge (Bandura 1982).
- Optimism, and the ability to use active coping strategies (Scheier and Carver 1992).
- The ability to take positive attitudes towards negative events (Scheier and Carver 1992).
- The belief that challenge brings personal development (Kobasa 1979).
- The ability to accept their limitations (Green 1986).
- The ability to make cognitive sense of experience, and not to see themselves as victims (Antonovsky 1987).

Tedeschi and Calhoun also claim that successful coping, and growth through traumatic experience, are related to extroversion and openness. The characteristics they record are almost identical to those discussed by Goleman (1996), mentioned in Chapter 1 when looking at emotional intelligence: a greater ability to cope with intimate relationships; good social skills, and gregariousness; the ability to express feelings openly; warmth and activeness.

Thus, what emerges from the research available is that the ability to cope with trauma seems to be related to personal characteristics, some of which are probably learned at a very early stage in life. Some strategies can certainly be learned from experience or via training (in the case of professionals). Since the most helpful ways of coping are related to the ability to talk about the experience, make some kind of sense of it and incorporate it into one's life, these should be the aims of any treatment offered to those who experience traumatic stress reactions.

4   Trauma and Treatment

Two major factors have influenced the understanding and treatment of post-traumatic stress and post-traumatic stress disorder: (1) the experience of war, and (2) the experience of disaster.

1   THE EXPERIENCE OF WAR

On D-Day in June 1944, a United States army psychiatrist sat with American soldiers on the beaches in Normandy and encouraged them to talk about their experiences. He came to believe that those who were able to talk in this informal way seemed more alert, more able to cope and more ready for combat the following day. Word of these informal 'debriefings' spread to other units and medical services, and psychiatrists began to use this system of informal talking to help soldiers to cope with combat. Research by Appel (1966) suggests that units that did not receive this kind of help had more psychiatric casualties than those that did. Also, when this 'talking therapy' was delayed until later, soldiers found it more difficult to return to active duty.

Combat stress is not a new phenomenon. It has certainly been identified for over two thousand years: the traumatic reactions of soldiers to war are recorded in historical incidents as early as the fourth century BC by Greek writers such as Herodotus. A common response has been to see these reactions as the result of fear; the Duke of Wellington, who acknowledged the power of fear in motivating the actions of soldiers, is recorded as having said:

'All soldiers run away. The good ones return.'

One of his generals, Sir Thomas Picton, who was killed at Waterloo, wrote to Wellington:

'My lord, I must give up. I am grown so nervous that when there is any service to be done it works upon my mind so that it is impossible for me to sleep at nights.' (as quoted in Holmes 1985)

During the American Civil War reactions to trauma were sometimes referred to as 'nostalgia', as though home-sickness or a yearning for the past were the cause. Soldiers' traumatic reactions to combat have been put down, as well as to fear, to cowardice, personality disorders, inadequacy, weakness and 'lack of moral fibre'—called LMF during the Second World War. In the First World War it seemed easier to put the blame on explosions ('shell-shock'), or on what was seen as mental weakness (war neurosis, trench hysteria or neurasthenia), or on weakness of character—in other words, 'cowardice'. During this war more than three hundred men were shot for military offences—over 260 of them for desertion—this constituted approximately 10 per cent of a total of over three thousand who were convicted. Only eighteen were shot for cowardice, since this was less easy to prove than desertion; the rest were executed for offences such as murder, striking superior officers, disobedience and mutiny (Putkowski and Sykes 1993). There was little understanding of the real reasons why men ran away or suffered from shell-shock, although some commentators were more enlightened than others. One army chaplain wrote home during the First World War:

'No words can tell you how I feel, nor can words tell you of the horrors of the clearing of a battlefield. This Battalion was left to do just that and several men went off with shell-shock and two more were wounded. I am certain that shell-shock was caused not just by the explosion of shells nearby, but by the sight, smell and horror of the battlefield in general. I felt dreadful.'

To this man it was clear that the cause was the sheer terror and carnage of warfare.

Not all traumatic reactions were the same. The novel *Regeneration* by Pat Barker (1992) is based on a real-life encounter between the poet Siegfried Sassoon and Dr W. H. R. Rivers, a neurologist, when Sassoon was receiving treatment at Craiglockhart Hospital in Scotland for his reactions to combat. Rivers suggests that the reactions of officers and of soldiers to trauma may be different—physical symptoms such as paralysis, blindness and deafness were all common in soldiers, but rare in officers. His rationale for this is that private soldiers belong to a stratum of society where physical symptoms are more acceptable than psychological ones. He mentions the case of mutism: since soldiers were not allowed to say what they thought, they might become totally mute. It was less unacceptable for officers to express their opinions, but because to do so would still be breaking their code of behaviour the result was more likely to be stammering (Rivers 1923). Rivers believed that the reactions were caused by the original battle trauma and not by any particular failure or weakness on the part of the sufferer.

External causes of traumatic reactions

Some have blamed explosions for the reactions suffered by combatants; others have looked for other causes.

Agent Orange

After the Vietnam War, some veterans believed that traumatic reactions were due to the effects of Agent Orange, the chemical sprayed from the air to defoliate the forests so that the enemy would be less able to hide there. This chemical caused deformities in unborn Vietnamese children, it was claimed, and so, the argument went, it was possible that it might affect the nervous systems of soldiers, causing symptoms such as nightmares, flash-backs, difficulty in maintaining relationships, inability to express emotions, hypersensitivity, outbursts of violence, depression, irritability, sleeplessness and an inability to show affection. It was easier to put the blame for such reactions on chemicals rather than to accept that they might be due to what was often diagnosed and described in medical records as 'personality disorder' or 'neurosis'. When post-traumatic stress disorder was officially defined for the first time in the *Diagnostic and Statistical Manual of Mental Disorders* of the American Psychiatric Association in 1980, traumatic reactions were finally recognised as the normal responses of soldiers to the acute stress of combat; in many cases, the recorded diagnosis was changed from 'personality disorder' to 'post-traumatic stress disorder'.

Gulf War syndrome

Consideration is being given at present to a condition called 'Gulf War syndrome'. A number of Gulf War veterans have experienced symptoms such as semi-paralysis of limbs and difficulty in walking, chronic fatigue, asthma, skin problems and sensitivity to certain chemicals, and some have developed cancer. Some claim that these are the result of injections and other medication given to the soldiers against tropical diseases, or the possible use of chemical or nerve agents by Iraq, or of the inhalation of toxic fumes from the burning oil wells. Others say that the effects are due to low-level nuclear radiation, or perhaps a combination of all of these. Could some reactions be due to the effects of traumatic stress?

In the USA, and now in the UK, some have claimed that there have also been genetic effects: the children of some Gulf War veterans have been born with physical deformities and abnormalities. However, at a conference in Kuwait in 1995 it was suggested that the number of children from veterans' families born with such defects is no different from the national averages for the same age groups. And the same may be true for the number of cancer victims. Nonetheless, some research in the UK has suggested that there have been effects on and changes in the nervous systems of veterans. The research is still unclear and requests have been made in this country for the Ministry of Defence to conduct its own investigations.

If it can be proved that there have been genetic as well as severe physical effects, then causes other than traumatic stress

will need to be considered. If not, then new symptoms will need
to be added to the list of possible reactions to trauma.

Influences on present-day treatment

Combat experience has influenced the kinds of treatment offered
to those who suffer from traumatic reactions. The basic response
is:

- To accept that reactions are normal.
- To give help as soon as possible.
- Not to treat the sufferer or casualty as weak or inadequate.

One of the sad things about the executions of soldiers during the
First World War—apart from the hurried trials, the lack of proper
representation, and the fact that most were probably suffering
from post-traumatic stress—is that the basic principles for coping
with combat stress were already understood by some military
doctors and psychiatrists, such as Dr Rivers. In fact, many thou-
sands of soldiers were helped to cope successfully with their
experiences. In an article in the *Lancet* (Rivers 1918) Dr Rivers
writes:

> It is natural to thrust aside painful memories just as it is natural
> to avoid dangerous or horrible scenes in actuality, and this
> natural tendency . . . is especially pronounced in those whose
> powers of resistance have been lowered by the long-continued
> strains of trench life, the shock of shell explosion, or other
> catastrophe of warfare.

He then records that this natural tendency to repress reactions is
further strengthened by the attitudes of relatives, friends, and
hospital staff:

> The advice which has usually been given to my patients in
> other hospitals is that they should endeavour to banish all
> thoughts of war from their minds. In some cases all conver-
> sation between patients or with visitors about the war is strictly
> forbidden, and the patients are instructed to lead their thoughts

to other topics, to beautiful scenery and other pleasant aspects
of experience.

Rivers describes this advice to suppress and repress thoughts
as an 'evil influence'. His method of treating patients was, on
the contrary, to encourage them to talk about their experiences,
no matter how horrific or terrifying, and by doing so to see them
in a new way. He also speaks of the influence and importance
of catharsis, re-education and what he refers to as 'faith and
suggestion'. Barker contrasts this approach with the work of a
doctor who used electro-convulsive shock therapy (ECT), and
gives a graphic account of the brutal and inhumane treatment of
a mute patient (Barker 1992, pp. 229ff). ECT sometimes worked,
but was often soon followed by a relapse. Rivers' approach shows
that humane treatment was available in those days, and that some,
at least, believed that traumatic reactions to combat were normal
and that it was helpful to talk about them.

The February 1918 issue of the *Lancet* referred to above
includes a number of articles about the psychological reactions
to warfare. According to one military psychiatrist, people who
can touch psychological wounds are rare, especially amongst
doctors; another writes about the predisposing factors of war
psychoneuroses and of the importance of considering the previous
character, background, temperament and experiences of sufferers.
After the First World War, many who continued to be diagnosed
as suffering from 'neurosis' never recovered, which suggests that
repression, labelling and hospitalisation had negative effects and
tended to reinforce the condition.

Even after the experiences of that war it was still believed by
many, doctors and psychiatrists included, that only the weak
suffered. A War Office inquiry report in 1922 decided that there
was no such thing as shell-shock. They recognised reactions such
as emotional shock and nervous exhaustion, but emphasised that
these were not reasons for men to fail to do their duty or to run
away. They did suggest that sufferers could be helped by keeping
them on the battlefield, allowing them to rest and talk, and prepar-

ing them for a return to duty by offering reassurance and encouragement.

This method of helping is known as:

Immediacy–Proximity–Expectancy.

'Immediacy' means that help should be offered as soon after the event as possible; 'Proximity', that the soldier is kept as close to the front line as possible and not treated like a hospital patient — he is allowed to rest and talk about his experiences, to wear his uniform and retain his weapons, and kept in touch with his comrades. 'Expectancy' means that it is expected that his reactions are due not to cowardice or weakness but to the stress of battle, and that he will soon recover and return to duty.

This method of treatment developed into what is sometimes known as 'the five Rs', because it involves:

- *Removal* from the immediate cause of the trauma.
- *Rest* and relaxation.
- *Recounting* through being allowed to talk.
- *Reassurance* that reactions are normal.
- *Return* to duty.

A sixth R could be added—*recovery*—for if the procedure is followed, most will recover. This method is now commonly used by many armies and other organisations, and the principles of rest, talking and reassurance lie behind many modern therapies.

Resistance to the idea of traumatic reactions

In spite of the growth in the understanding of the nature of trauma, there is still a common belief that reactions are due to character deficiencies. Within the military environment, the powerful macho image and the need to perform prevent some from accepting that traumatic reactions can be normal. Officers may see such reactions in their men as signs not only of weakness, but also of their own failure as leaders to provide the right training or quality of leadership. The prevailing attitude is that an officer should not allow his men to fail. And when such reactions occur in the officer himself, he may find it impossible to accept or admit it, which can further harden defences. Military training engenders a very necessary solidarity, a sense of comradeship, but traumatic reactions can be exacerbated by the belief that a soldier should not let his friends down or show signs of weakness. Such defences often mean that the soldier will cope; but the disadvantage is that they can make it difficult not only for others to offer treatment, but also for those who need it to ask for or accept help. Similar problems occur in other uniformed organisations such as the police, fire and rescue and ambulance services.

2   THE EXPERIENCE OF DISASTER

Historical records of traumatic reactions are not confined to warfare. Reactions to the Great Fire of London in 1666 are mentioned in his diary by Samuel Pepys, and Charles Dickens wrote of his involvement in a train crash. A number of major disasters have influenced the understanding of trauma and the nature of treatment.

Crisis intervention theory

In the Cocoanut Grove Night-club fire in 1943 in Boston, Massachusetts, some four hundred people perished. Dr Eric Lindemann worked with the survivors and relatives of the dead (Lindemann 1944), and his work was later developed by Dr Gerald Caplan and others (Caplan 1964). From this, crisis intervention theory evolved. Crisis intervention methods are still developing, but the findings of Lindemann and Caplan are basic to the way in which treatment is offered today. As with the experience of warfare, treatment seems to have evolved from the immediate needs of victims as well as from later research and understanding.

At the centre of crisis intervention theory is Caplan's concept of *homoeostasis*, which envisages a balance between the cognitive and emotional aspects of human experience. As we grow and develop, a balance is achieved between our ability to reason, think and cope and our emotional responses. Each person's homoeostatic balance is different, because human beings are different from each other and because they respond to events in different ways. Physiologically, traumatic reactions can be seen as an imbalance between different organs of the body in which, under stress, some become more aroused and stressed than others. This imbalance causes reactions which may become increasingly difficult to cope with, and normal stress may develop into dys-stress. The person under stress attempts to recall and use coping mechanisms from previous experiences. If these mechanisms and strategies are not appropriate or effective in achieving the right homoeostatic balance, they can lead to an emotional crisis or breakdown. Caplan believed that in most cases this balance would be restored normally, and usually within a month or so. But if this did not happen, further crises could develop and might lead to the development of more disturbing or disabling symptoms.

If the right kind of help is offered the individual will usually recover, and homoeostatic balance will be restored. This help should come:

- From early intervention.
- By reinforcing and strengthening any successful coping skills already being used.
- By learning new and more effective methods for coping.

The crisis intervention model recognises four possible stages of reactions:

Stage 1: Impact
This stage takes place within the first few minutes and hours. It focuses on the initial effects of the incident and on the reactions of the person involved. There can be disorientation and a tendency either to stay or to run away—the 'fight or flight' effect. This stage takes into account any previous events that the person involved has experienced, and how they may affect his or her present reactions; looking at the main emotions and feelings, and how these influence behaviour, is important. Intervention comes through allowing immediate ventilation of feelings and reactions and thereby reducing anxiety.

Stage 2: Withdrawal and confusion

After a few days, people may be depressed, deny that they have any reactions or feelings, and experience a sense of detachment and unreality. Help is offered through considering the available resources and by offering a task-orientated plan of action.

Stage 3: Adjustment

Usually adjustment takes place after four to six weeks. At this stage emotional and other reactions are being acknowledged, and there may be positive feelings of hope which should be built upon and reinforced.

Stage 4: Reconstruction

During this stage there is usually a growth in confidence and in positive thoughts about the future. Some assessment of the need for on-going support or counselling may be given by a therapist.

So crisis intervention theory offers some understanding of why reactions occur, and suggests methods of treatment.

Three more recent incidents in the USA, all airline crashes, emphasised the disastrous effects that traumatic reactions can have on both victims and helpers: one was in San Diego in 1978 in a residential area, another near Chicago in 1979, and the third into the Potomac river in January 1982. Those involved in all three incidents continued to experience traumatic stress reactions for some time after the event. After the Potomac incident it was decided to instigate the first formal structuring of Critical Incident Stress Debriefing, using the Jeffrey Mitchell model (Mitchell 1983) and based on a crisis intervention cognitive–emotive structure.

Crisis intervention ideas and strategies are similar to those developed from the experience of combat.

OTHER THEORIES

Three theories used in counselling and therapy can also be related to an understanding of traumatic reactions and to the treatment offered:

1 Transactional analysis.
2 The Carkhuff and Egan three-stage counselling model.
3 The bereavement counselling model.

Each of these offers understanding and suggestions for treatment similar to those developed from the experience of war and disaster.

1 Transactional analysis

Transactional analysis (Berne 1968; Harris 1973) is based on the belief that human beings operate at any given time in one or more of three modes, or 'ego states': adult–child–parent. The adult is capable, thinking, logical and rational; the child carries the emotional responses; the parent is nurturing, caring and supportive. During and after a traumatic experience an individual will often try to cope in the adult mode, by being realistic and objective; there will also be emotional reactions, in the child mode, which may be suppressed; and the parent mode will result in the use of previously learned coping skills and supportive strategies. Using methods developed from the experience of combat and disaster, reactions are accepted as normal for the individual concerned, who is asked to tell the story of what happened (adult mode), allowed to express feelings (child mode), and encouraged to seek and use both internal and external support mechanisms (parent mode).

2 The Carkhuff and Egan three-stage counselling model

This model (Egan 1990), familiar to many counsellors, suggests that the most effective method of intervention is by working through three stages: exploring the situation as extensively as possible; understanding what has happened and why; and then considering what action can be taken. This exploration–

understanding–action model involves accepting reactions as normal, encouraging people to talk about their experiences and express feelings, and offering reassurance and support.

3 The bereavement counselling model

The classic four-stage model of reactions to bereavement is that of shock–anger–depression–recovery: the initial shock; the expression of emotions; the expression of feelings of sadness, or depression; and then, hopefully, a move towards renewal and healing. Grief is seen as a normal and necessary response to the loss, and as a process which needs encouragement and support. Once again, this involves accepting the normality of reactions and encouraging people to talk and express their feelings and emotions as a way through to healing; and then offering support, reassurance and hope.

In these three approaches there are parallels not only with the strategies used after experiences of combat and disaster, but also with the Critical Incident Debriefing models described later.

BASIC BELIEFS AND STRATEGIES

When devising methods for helping victims of traumatic incidents, professional helpers, whether counsellors, psychiatrists, psychologists or psychotherapists, have developed a number of basic beliefs:

- Traumatic reactions are normal responses and not signs of weakness or inadequacy.
- Victims, unless physically injured, should not be hospitalised or treated as patients in any way.
- Help should be offered at an early stage.
- Talking about traumatic experiences helps.
- Help should be offered not only to the immediate victims, but also to rescuers and carers and, if necessary, to their families.
- Victims need to be able to make cognitive sense of their

experiences and to sort out the resulting confusion.

- Information should be given about what has happened and about what help is available for individuals, groups and, where relevant, families.
- People should return to normal duty or work as soon as possible.
- It should be expected that most people will recover within a short time.
- Helpers should offer empathic understanding, but also positive support and reassurance by encouraging self-confidence and using personal as well as external resources.

In addition there are other factors that apply especially to organisations professionally involved in dealing with trauma and its aftermath:

- Rescuers and helpers need psychological preparation, through education and training about possible traumatic responses.
- Organisations should include education about trauma and stress as part of everyone's training.
- Organisations should be aware of the kind of help and support needed during an incident, as well as afterwards.
- Peer, colleague, organisational and family support is important.
- On-going support and assessment are helpful.

Treatment is offered in a number of ways that derive from these basic beliefs and strategies.

METHODS OF HELPING

The usual methods of helping after traumatic experiences are:

1 Talking and catharsis.
2 Counselling.
3 Critical Incident Debriefing.

1 Talking and catharsis

The simplest way of helping is for those involved in a traumatic event to sit down and talk about it with a colleague, friend, family member or professional therapist. Such expressions as 'Get it off your chest', 'Let it all hang out', 'A problem shared is a problem halved', 'Don't bottle things up inside you' are appropriate here. But *problems* of one sort or another may arise.

Not wanting to talk

Not all will feel that talking about emotions helps—some will say that some things are better left alone and will not want to open what might be seen as a Pandora's Box. This view needs to be respected. Also, catharsis by means of talking does not mean that the feelings and emotions will disappear. The individual may well feel better for a while, but the feelings may return and she may then feel worse. Helping is not just a process of catharsis or of exorcising feelings and experiences: it should include incorporating the emotional reactions into the individual's life, such that some understanding and ability to interpret them positively result.

The stiff upper lip

Western, and particularly British, culture does not make it easy to express emotions and feelings. It is commonly held that, in the past, support from families and neighbours was always forthcoming. This may have been true in some cases, but on the whole it is probably a myth, for it could be argued that individuals were in fact encouraged to keep things to themselves, or in the family, and to cope without 'going on about it'. Similarly, it is often said that when soldiers returned from the Second World War they talked through their experiences with comrades, family or friends and so did not need counselling or psychiatric help. This, too, is probably a myth. Some did talk, but many who returned from the war were expected to quietly go home and get on with their lives—and this is exactly what they did. Also, those at home had experienced their own traumas and problems, and were often not able to listen, or to offer help or understanding. Some ex-service personnel do talk about their war experiences, but this mainly takes the form of remembering exciting or humorous incidents. Far-Eastern prisoners of war share with comrades a deep bond of affection, but when they meet for reunions they rarely talk about the trauma or the atrocities that they witnessed and experienced.

Anger and guilt

Anger is often seen as a destructive emotion that should be controlled. But the popularity of the character Victor Meldrew in the British TV series, *One Foot in the Grave*, seems to show that deep down many people would like to be more able to express how angry they sometimes feel. Meldrew certainly does—he is almost constantly angry, aggressive and irritable. Some people say that we should not entertain feelings of anger, but that we should forgive and forget. The Second World War, they may say, is a long time ago and we should bury the past and think of the future, so that within a short while we will, or should, 'get over it'. Similarly, if, in combat, you have killed people, experienced torture and terror, seen the mutilated bodies of comrades or women and children, this, some say, is all just part of the job that you were trained for. To feel guilty, angry, shocked or upset is negative thinking. Some can indeed push their experiences away and deny such feelings. Any emotion they do feel usually concerns the deaths of comrades or results from a sense of pride in their unit or country and in what they have achieved.

Thus, well ingrained beliefs and ideas, and group and social pressures, seem to ensure that most people, especially men, find great difficulty in talking about their feelings. The British stiff upper lip is still very powerful.

After a presentation on post-trauma stress, an ex-police sergeant remarked that he had never suffered from stress or trauma during the whole of his service. He had seen dead bodies of every kind and in almost every situation, and experienced horrific scenes, he said, but these had never affected him. When asked what he did after particularly horrific events, he said, 'Well, often I couldn't sleep properly for weeks.' When pressed further, he added, 'I would go home and talk to my wife, sometimes until two or three o'clock in the morning.' He still maintained that he was not affected by trauma in any way, claiming that there was no such thing as stress. One person asked him how his wife coped!

In spite of these defences and the problems they create, many would agree that talking and expressing feelings can and does help, especially in a safe environment with someone who can be trusted and who listens and understands.

2   Counselling

Methods have been developed for use with both individuals and groups based on a general counselling approach. Sessions take place in a safe and confidential environment, with a professional counsellor or therapist encouraging people to talk about their experiences. The story of what happened is built up, and participants are encouraged to express their feelings. Some counsellors and therapists will attempt to relate people's reactions to previous experiences of trauma or other, early life, events. Such an approach can be on-going and may lead to further counselling sessions.

Counselling can be effective because it allows people to express what they feel, and helps to reassure them that their reactions are normal. Also, the presence of an empathic, non-judgemental and accepting counsellor or therapist can be useful in itself. However, there can be *problems*. Since models are usually unstructured, with facts and feelings expressed as and when they surface, people can still be left confused. Counselling does not necessarily help them to integrate their experiences; they may be unable to see either where their feelings originate, or where they belong in the incident.

3   Critical Incident Debriefing

Critical Incident (Stress) Debriefing is based on crisis intervention theory and on the experiences of Dr Jeffrey Mitchell with fire officers and disasters in the USA. Psychological Debriefing, a term for a similar model, was developed by Dr Atle Dyregrov in Norway. Then there is the Critical Incident Debriefing Revised Model of Facts, Feelings and Future used in Britain. In all three models, people are encouraged to tell their story without letting feelings intrude. Next, they talk about sensory impressions and reactions, and about how they felt at the time and how they feel now. They are then given reassurance and information about possible future reactions and resources for helping, and any need for support or referral is considered. These models will be described in detail in later chapters.

The advantages of Debriefing are that the structure encourages a better understanding of the experience in question by separating the telling of the story from the feelings generated by the incident. It offers a *cognitive restructuring* of the incident in the minds of those involved, so that they can make more sense of what has happened. This should help to resolve some of the confusion generated, and also enable people to understand whatever might trigger reactions in the future.

> A woman involved in an armed robbery became frightened every time she saw a man carrying a brown paper parcel in the street. Through the Debriefing process she was able to realise that her response was connected with the fact that the man who had carried out the robbery had been carrying a brown paper parcel, which he claimed was concealing a shotgun.

> A woman who had been raped could not drink or even stand the smell of coffee for weeks afterwards. From the detail resurrected by the Debriefing she remembered that when she was raped a coffee percolator had been bubbling away in the background and the smell had pervaded the whole of the office where it had happened. She could then connect her experience of rape with the smell of coffee, and was more able to cope. She began to drink coffee again.

Critical Incident Debriefing as a form of intervention was originally offered to people, either as individuals or as groups, after major disasters, but the model has been extended to include any incident that contains violence, death or shock, and trauma.

But there can be *problems* with labels. 'Critical Incident Stress Debriefing' displeases those who feel that the word 'stress' is threatening, so some omit it and call the procedure 'Critical Incident Debriefing'. 'Psychological Debriefing' is problematical for those who associate the word 'psychological' with stigma and with images of psychiatrists and psychological assessment. And the word 'debriefing' itself means different things to different people. Soldiers and police officers use it—often in the form of 'Operational Debriefing'—to mean an informal or formal session following an exercise or incident. Furthermore, some think that Critical Incident Debriefing is a form of counselling, and this misperception can entail some resistance to the method. Critical Incident Debriefing should not be confused either with Operational Debriefing or with counselling.

It was mentioned in the Introduction that there is some concern that Debriefing might result in re-traumatisation. But this can be said of any form of help, therapy or counselling—even of talking to a friend or family member. In fact, most approaches involve re-traumatisation in that the traumatic experience and reactions to it are usually resurrected. But hopefully, these will not be overwhelming and will not lead to the need for medical or psychiatric help. If they do, it would probably have been needed eventually, anyway.

Resistance
Experience with professional helpers and rescuers recognises certain critical areas:

- Training.
- Preparation—practical and emotional.
- Dealing with the incident itself.
- Operational Debriefing.
- Offering counselling and therapy.

The training that professionals receive, and the closely knit comradeship, support and professionalism that it engenders, help them to cope and survive. It also prepares them physically and emotionally, and this builds up with time and experience. When an incident is over it is usual to have an Operational Debriefing, which is concerned almost entirely with practical issues. Often, at the end of this Debriefing counselling or support is offered to those who feel they need it, and any who develop symptoms of stress can go for help. The problem is that the traumatic nature of the incident, the shock, denial and adherence to the macho image, often make it impossible for those who do suffer to ask for help. Only when symptoms have developed and there are problems with health and absenteeism, and personal, marital or other relationship difficulties, do some seek help.

> After a series of shootings and a subsequent hostage situation, the consultant psychiatrist who attended the scene suggested to the senior police officer present that when they held the Operational Debriefing the officers should be told that counsellors and a psychiatrist were available. This was done, but no police officer self-referred or sought help. The psychiatrist was convinced that some officers developed problems as a result of their experiences.

In this structure, counselling is seen as an optional extra only for those who either feel that, or look as though, they need help. The trouble here is that the way people react is not necessarily a guide to how they are coping: those who are crying or expressing their emotions in some other way may in fact be the ones who are coping best. Those who are tightly controlling their emotions now may explode or suffer days, weeks, months or even years later. Because of this, Mitchell looked for a form of intervention that could be used between the Operational Debriefing and counselling—for all those involved, not just for those who *appeared* to need help. This procedure was Critical Incident Debriefing.

Critical Incident Debriefing is preventive and proactive: preventive because it attempts to reduce the possibility of problems developing at a later stage; proactive because it is offered as a normal procedure within an organisation. Those who develop reactions can self-refer as necessary, and all should be aware of the support available to them should they need it.

TREATMENTS OFFERED FOR POST-TRAUMATIC STRESS AND PTSD

There is a difference between help offered immediately after an incident through informal talking, counselling or Critical Incident Debriefing and the treatment given at a later stage when further, deeper symptoms have developed or when PTSD has been diagnosed. Some methods of PTSD treatment originated in the United States as 'trauma reduction' therapies, especially from the experience of helping Vietnam veterans. Muss (1991) has developed a trauma-reduction process in which the sufferer is helped to visualise the trauma as a story in a video or film that is played forwards and then backwards. This takes the client from before the incident when all was well, into the trauma, and then back to the safety of the pre-incident situation. Shapiro (1989) has developed an eye-movement procedure for desensitising people, which involves the therapist moving a finger backwards and forwards from left to right in front of the client's eyes while he visualises the trauma.

The more widely used methods of treatment for PTSD, or combinations of treatments, are:

- *Behavioural therapy* Includes systematic desensitisation; exposure to the fear, flooding and exposure techniques; training in stress reduction and relaxation.
- *Cognitive therapy and cognitive restructuring* Aim to correct unreasonable, distorted and unhelpful beliefs and create better understanding.
- *Psychotherapy and psychodynamic counselling* Attempt to deal with the anxiety caused by the incident and with any defence mechanisms used; this duo also looks at hidden feelings and reactions due to previous traumatic life experiences.
- *Cognitive–behavioural therapy* Problem-orientated and directive, using techniques such as desensitisation and event-restructuring.

- *Group therapy* Often includes residential care, individual therapy, education, exercise and outdoor physical activities.
- *Medication* Often used in conjunction with other treatments.

Scott and Stradling (1992) report that a study by Keane *et al.* (1989) of Vietnam veterans suggests that those who received help generally showed a decrease in symptoms of re-experiencing and arousal, but not of avoidance behaviour. Blake (1993), having looked at eight studies comparing different kinds of treatment, concludes that all forms of treatment appear to reduce some symptoms. He reports that so-called 'positive' symptoms such as anger and intrusive thoughts, startle responses, arousal and nightmares seem to be reduced, but that 'negative' reactions such as avoidance behaviour, denial, numbing and feelings of isolation are more difficult to deal with. For those with PTSD it may be that different treatments are more effective at different points in the development of the condition. Also, since people's reactions to incidents differ, treatment may need to be flexible in order to meet the differences both in personal characteristics and in the diversity of symptoms. What does emerge is that avoidance behaviour seems more resistant to therapy than other reactions.

Cognitive–behavioural therapy—integration, not exorcism
There is a growing belief that cognitive–behavioural treatments are the most effective for most people. Psychotherapy and counselling can help but, according to Herman (1992), neither gets rid of trauma, and the goal of recounting the trauma story must be integration, not exorcism. It is not sufficient for people to tell their stories and express their feelings. They need to be able to restructure the critical event in their lives and give it some kind of meaning; to discover new ways of interpreting it, and of coping with their reactions, with themselves and with their experiences.

Meichenbaum (1994) suggests that people who experience traumatic events try to find new ways of understanding their experiences by restructuring their beliefs, thoughts and ideas into what he calls new 'schemes'. 'Schemes', according to this Canadian psychologist, are the ways in which each individual learns to interpret and cope with life in general and that have been developing throughout his life. When they are challenged or disturbed, he attempts to acquire new ways of looking at himself and at the world, and to interpret what happened and why he behaved and reacted to the incident in question as he did. Meichenbaum's approach to the treatment of PTSD is in five stages, each with its own goals for intervention.

Stage 1
The goals are, first, to establish a good therapeutic relationship with the client and, second, to encourage him to tell his story in his own way and in his own time. Any feelings expressed should be acknowledged and supported, and the need for physical comfort, safety and rest should be considered. The client's present strengths should be assessed, and some information about PTSD given. His reactions should be seen as normal and natural, and there should be an element of hope for the future.

Stage 2
The client should be helped to make some sense of his story, and this should result in reducing the level of his reactions. New coping skills, which must be related to the symptoms, can be taught. Reactions such as re-experiencing, avoidance behaviour and arousal should be treated with cognitive–behavioural methods, and medication should be considered as a possible option.

Stage 3
The therapist should continue to help the client to make sense of the event through cognitive restructuring; try to ensure that he eventually experiences some element of control when telling the story. Further cognitive–behavioural treatments are used to expose the client to the trauma and to rebuild or replace shattered beliefs. There should also be some feelings of personal growth and positive learning; personal resources within the client should be encouraged and used.

Stage 4
The client should be able to re-establish relationships with family and friends, and regain feelings of trust. There should be no possibility of re-victimisation, and he may even start to help others who have suffered comparable experiences; he should begin to regain and rebuild any lost confidence.

Stage 5
Self-confidence should increase, and future strategies for preventing any relapse should be discussed. Further sessions, if needed, should be considered and arranged.

Meichenbaum's goals can be summarised as follows:

- To reassure the client that his reactions are normal.
- To help him to recognise stress responses and triggers; to help him to understand why and how he reacts as he does, and to recover some element of control over his life and his reactions.
- To help him to make sense of his experiences and reactions, and to nurture the feeling that he is coping and can integrate his experiences into his life.
- To inspire hope—frequently, victims feel that there is none. It should be emphasised that, though he will never forget, and though the trauma is ineradicably part of his experience of life, he can nonetheless learn to cope.

The main point of looking at the various approaches to understanding traumatic reactions and methods of treatment, discussed above, is to ask if they are related to the Critical Incident Debriefing process. The answer is that they are: Critical Incident Debriefing incorporates the main elements of those different models and theories in its emphasis on:

- Accepting reactions as normal responses to trauma.
- Creating a safe and confidential environment.
- Allowing people to talk and tell their stories.

- Encouraging a better cognitive understanding by reducing confusion and helping to integrate the story into personal experience.
- Allowing feelings to emerge and be expressed and firmly placing them where they belong in the incident.
- Educating people about traumatic reactions and coping strategies.
- Encouraging the understanding of reactions, offering hope where necessary and providing personal, group and organisational support.

All of these aims are considered important by most therapists of whatever persuasion, and are basic to the Debriefing model and method. Harig and Sprenger (1995), in a paper given at a mental health conference in Kuwait, state:

The disorders of extreme stress recalled in survivors . . . require that therapists listen to their clients' stories with patience, respect, and compassion, that they give credence to what they say, and that they provide a safe and secure place to revisit their traumas; that they help them reframe the expectations and attributions which were shaped in the traumatic experience; and that they guide them towards coping skills which help their clients to integrate and adapt their experiences into the present.

These are the objectives of Critical Incident Debriefing.

5   Demobilisation, Defusing and Debriefing

In the USA in the early 1980s, Jeffrey Mitchell initiated three approaches to helping professionals and others after critical incidents and disasters:

1   Demobilisation.
2   Defusing.
3   Critical Incident Stress Debriefing

The nature and length of the incident and the number of people involved determine which of these methods is used. They are outlined here in brief, but defusing and Critical Incident Debriefing are explained in full later. Details of Mitchell's original models can be found in *Critical Incident Stress Debriefing: An Operations Manual* (Mitchell and Everly 1995).

In the USA Mitchell has organised critical incident stress management (CISM) teams, largely to help emergency services personnel. CISM teams consist of a leader, who is always a mental health professional, assisted by peer supporters who are normally other professionals such as chaplains, social workers and counsellors.

1   DEMOBILISATION

Demobilisation is a procedure used after major disasters when there are large numbers of people to be dealt with. It normally takes from ten to twenty minutes. The aims—all similar to those of defusing and Debriefing—are:

- To provide a gradual return from involvement in a traumatic incident to normal life.

- To reduce the level of reactions.
- To give people a brief opportunity to talk and ask questions.
- To give information about possible future reactions.
- To provide information about coping methods.

Demobilisation takes place immediately an incident is over. The participants first attend a short talk in one room, where they sit in small groups around prearranged tables, at each of which a trained member of the CISM team gives a ten-minute talk on the incident, on the normality of psychological reactions and on strategies for coping. Next, the demobiliser allows a short time for people to talk or ask questions; they are given hand-outs with information about traumatic reactions and the support available. They then move into another room for ten to fifteen minutes, where they are allowed to rest and are given food and non-alcoholic drinks before going back on or off duty. Mitchell claims to have used this procedure successfully after a number of major incidents.

2   DEFUSING

Defusing (see Summary 1) is a shortened form of Debriefing, lasting approximately forty-five minutes to an hour, although it can take longer, depending on reactions to the incident and to the defusing procedure itself. It is usually conducted immediately after the incident. In contrast, Debriefing is not carried out until 36–48 hours have elapsed, and can take up to four hours. Mitchell tends to use Debriefing with large groups of people, often from different organisations, and defusing with small groups who normally work together. The aims of defusing are similar to those of Debriefing, but the process does not go as deeply into emotions and feelings. Defusers can be peer supporters, clergy or other professionals trained for the task, and mental health professionals need not attend. Defusing always takes place at some distance from the scene so as to create a neutral and safe environment. All those involved are always defused before going off duty.

Summary 1: The Mitchell defusing model

		Time 45 mins–1 hour
1	Introduction	Defuser introduces himself.
		Explains that the session is confidential, not investigative.
		Explains the aims:

- To reduce levels of immediate reactions.
- To normalise the experience.
- To create solidarity in the group.
- To restore cognitive processes.
- To give information and reassurance.
- To reduce the need or prepare for a Critical Incident Debriefing.

2	Exploration	'What happened?'
		'What did you do?'
		'How did you react?'
		'How do you feel now?'
		Defusees tell their story.
3	Information	Defuser gives information about possible future reactions, and about what support is available, should help be needed.
		Issues information leaflets and hand-outs.
Decide:		Is a Critical Incident Debriefing necessary?

There are three parts to a defusing:

1	Introduction	5 minutes
2	Exploration	30 minutes
3	Information	10 minutes

1   Introduction
The defuser introduces himself, explains that the defusing is confidential and not investigative, and then outlines the aims of the defusing and of the procedure.

2   Exploration
Participants are encouraged to talk about what happened, what they did, and what their reactions were and are now. Anyone who wants to speak may do so.

3   Information
The defuser gives information about possible future reactions, the intention being to normalise reactions, to look at coping strategies and to give information about support.

If the session is long and reactions are strong, a decision will be made to hold a Critical Incident Stress Debriefing at a later stage. When the defusing is over, the defuser provides follow-up by contacting team members—especially any who might need help or who were particularly distressed or defensive about talking or taking part.

3   CRITICAL INCIDENT STRESS DEBRIEFING

There are three main Debriefing models:

1   The original Mitchell model.
2   The Dyregrov model.
3   The revised model.

1   The Mitchell model
Critical Incident Stress Debriefing should not take place until 36–48 hours have elapsed after the incident, but can be conducted up to eight weeks afterwards—and some use the model at a much later point. The problem with delayed Debriefing is that facts and emotions can become mixed up with previous and subsequent events. The numbers attending a Debriefing can vary from four to twenty, but Mitchell prefers groups to be larger rather than smaller. The structure of the original Mitchell model is the basis for both the Dyregrov model and the revised model. The Mitchell model is in seven stages, and takes two and a half hours or more (see Summary 2).

Summary 2: The Mitchell Debriefing model

	Time	2 hours plus
1	Introduction	Debriefer/co-debriefer introduce themselves. Debriefer explains aim and purpose of the debriefing. Explains rules, stressing confidentiality.
2	Facts	'What happened?' 'What did you do?' 'How did others treat you?' 'How did the incident end?'
3	Thoughts	'What did you think?' 'What did you do, and why?'
4	Reactions	'How did you feel in the beginning, and later?' 'What was the worst thing about it for you?' 'How do you feel now?'
5	Symptoms	'What physical and emotional reactions did you experience, at the time and later?'
6	Teaching	Debriefer emphasises the normality of their reactions. Prepares the debriefees for possible future reactions. 'What have you learned?'
7	Re-entry	What support is needed? What support is available? 'Any questions?' Issues information and support leaflets. Remains available when the Debriefing is over. Follow-up essential; referral as necessary.

Stage 1: Introduction
The debriefer outlines his own experience and explains the purpose of the Debriefing: to reduce the level of distressing effects; to allow ventilation of feelings; to help the participants to make some sense of the incident and of their reactions, and to use their own strengths or the strengths of the group to reduce tension and any feelings of abnormality. The rules are then explained—with special emphasis on the fact that nobody is forced to speak and that the session is confidential.

Stage 2: Facts
Here the object is to build up a comprehensive picture of what happened and of what each person did during the incident. Questions avoid the area of emotional reactions: the emphasis is on thoughts and facts, not feelings.

Stage 3: Thoughts
The focus is on what people thought during the incident and what their impressions were and are now.

Stage 4: Reactions
Questions focus on feelings and emotional reactions—this is usually the longest stage.

Stage 5: Symptoms
The aim is to continue to create a gradual transition from the incident back to normality: a return from the emotional to the cognitive. The emphasis is on showing that whatever reactions or feelings have been experienced, both during and after the event, they are normal.

Stage 6: Teaching
This stage is a further move towards cognitive understanding. It continues to emphasise the normality of reactions, prepares people for any future reactions and looks at strategies for coping. The debriefer can also ask if there are any feelings of growth or positive learning.

Stage 7: Re-entry

This stage looks at the future and at support, and gives an opportunity for any questions to be raised. A brief summary of the session follows, and hand-outs are offered giving details of reactions to trauma and the telephone numbers of people and agencies offering support.

Follow-up, referral and counselling

Mitchell makes it clear that follow-up is essential and that when the Debriefing is concluded, it is not over. The debriefer should stay with the group informally for a while, and be available should anyone wish to talk. There may be a need for referral to counsellors or to other professionals. Serving refreshments after the Debriefing gives an opportunity for the debriefer to be available in an informal atmosphere for further questions and discussion.

After the Debriefing, the CISD team meets for their own debriefing, to discuss what happened and to offer each other support.

2   The Dyregrov model: Psychological Debriefing

The original Mitchell model was adapted by Dyregrov (1989) and called 'Psychological Debriefing'. It takes at least three hours. There are slight differences between it and the original model. Dyregrov defines Debriefing as:

> a group meeting to review the impressions and reactions that survivors, bereaved or helpers experience during or following critical incidents, accidents and disasters. The meeting aims at reducing unnecessary psychological after-effects.

Dyregrov acknowledges that crisis intervention methods form the basis for the model. These are:

- *Rapid outreach*   The Debriefing should not be done on the same day as the incident, or the next day, because participants are usually in a state of shock and heavily defended against talking. The Psychological Debriefing should reach out to and include all those involved in the incident, whether as professionals, rescuers or immediate victims.

• *Focusing on the present*   The main focus is on present reactions, although previous experiences are important in determining how people will react. Feelings and emotions from the incident and from previous and present experiences may emerge.

• *Mobilisation of resources*   The group format of a Debriefing is mutually supportive, but the Debriefing can also be used with individuals. Organisations should include the procedure in their reaction routine.

Dyregrov argues that, if there is resistance to Debriefing from those in positions of authority within the organisation concerned, they should be shown the benefits—which, he claims, include a more rapid return to work and normality and fewer personal problems at home and at work. The financial as well as the practical and psychological benefits should also be stressed.

The *structure* of Dyregrov's model (Summary 3) is similar to Mitchell's, although different names are used for some of the seven stages:

Mitchell	Dyregrov
1 Introduction	1 Introduction
2 Facts	2 Expectations and facts
3 Thoughts	3 Thoughts and sensory impressions
4 Reactions	4 Emotional reactions
5 Symptoms	5 Normalisation
6 Teaching	6 Future planning and coping
7 Re-entry	7 Disengagement

The differences are that the reactions and symptoms phases of the Mitchell model figure jointly under emotional reactions in the Dyregrov model, and more time is usually spent on normalisation and future planning and coping. Dyregrov emphasises the importance of the introduction for setting the scene and outlining

Summary 3: The Dyregrov Debriefing model

	Time	3 hours plus
1	Introduction	Debriefer/co-debriefer introduce themselves. Debriefer explains aim and purpose of the Debriefing. Explains rules, stressing confidentiality.
2	Expectations and facts	'What did you expect?' 'What happened?' 'How did others treat you?' 'How did the incident end?'
3	Thoughts and sensory impressions	'What did you think in the beginning, and later?' 'What did you do, and why?' 'What sights, sounds, smells, tastes, touch sensations did you experience?'
4	Emotional reactions	'How did you feel in the beginning, and later?' 'What was the worst thing about it for you?' 'How do you feel now?'
5	Normalisation	Debriefer reassures debriefees of the normality of their reactions. Explains possible reactions.
6	Future planning and coping	'What help do you (or your family) need?' 'What support do you (or your family) need?' 'What have you learned?'
7	Disengagement	'Any questions?' Issues information and support leaflets. Remains available for help and support when Debriefing is over. Follow-up and referral, as necessary.

the procedure. He also concentrates on sensory impressions as a trigger and transition stage from the thoughts stage to the emotional reactions stage.

The Dyregrov model is briefly outlined here (some stages are described in detail later when the revised model is explained).

Stage 1: Introduction

The debriefer outlines his experience and explains the purpose of the Debriefing. He stresses that Debriefing should lessen the possibility of disturbing and difficult reactions developing at a later stage. The rules are explained and each person is asked to say how he learned about the incident, how he came to be there and what his role was at the time.

Stage 2: Expectations and facts

This section looks at the story of the incident as experienced and perceived by the debriefees, but they are not encouraged to talk about emotions.

Stage 3: Thoughts and sensory impressions

The focus is on what people thought, what their impressions were, what they did and what happened. Sensory impressions are discussed—sights, sounds, touch, taste and smell. Dyregrov believes that concentrating on sensory impressions, as well as acting as a bridge between the facts and the emotional reactions, helps to prevent disturbing reactions emerging or being triggered and exerting control over the present.

Stage 4: Emotional reactions

The debriefer asks questions about feelings such as fear, anger, helplessness, frustration, self-reproach and guilt—or whatever has emerged in telling the story. The reactions of partners, family, colleagues and friends are also discussed.

Stage 5: Normalisation

The debriefer stresses the normality of feelings and other reactions, and gives examples of possible reactions that might emerge later. Dyregrov calls this 'anticipatory guidance'.

Stage 6: Future planning and coping
The possibility of needing help and support for the participants and for their families, colleagues and others is discussed, beginning with individuals, moving on to the group, and then to the external resources available.

Stage 7: Disengagement
This section gives an opportunity for questions to be raised and for the debriefer to give guidance about coping with possible future reactions.

Follow-up, referral and counselling
Information is offered about follow-up and access to counselling, and a list of helpful contact names and telephone numbers is given. The debriefer can offer and make available ongoing help and support as appropriate.

Dyregrov (1989) commends the procedure for use with both groups and individuals. He adds that debriefers should be familiar with group processes, have knowledge of post-traumatic stress reactions and of coping strategies. He concludes:

> Psychological Debriefings accelerate the recovery of normal people experiencing normal reactions to abnormal events.

3   The revised model: Facts–Feelings–Future

The revised model, outlined in detail from Chapter 9 onwards, is based on the experience of using and teaching the models of Mitchell and Dyregrov and has been developed and modified over a number of years. The structure has been simplified into three central stages—Facts–Feelings–Future—plus an introduction and an ending: it incorporates the seven stages of Mitchell and Dyregrov but combines the facts and thoughts stages and the reaction and re-entry stages. It concentrates more than do its predecessors on what was happening before the incident took place. The model has been described as 'the three Fs'.

The three models relate as follows:

Mitchell	Dyregrov	Revised model
Introduction	Introduction	Introduction
Facts	Facts	Facts
Thoughts	Thoughts and sensory impressions	
Reactions	Emotional reactions	Feelings
Symptoms	Normalisation	Future
Teaching	Future planning and coping	
Re-entry	Disengagement	Ending

There are other models, most of which are adaptations of the original Mitchell and Dyregrov models. The Raphael model (Raphael 1986) is more person-centred and less cognitively based than those of Mitchell and Dyregrov. The 'post office model' (Tehrani and Westlake 1994) was developed for use with individuals, but is similar to the Dyregrov and Mitchell models.

6   Simple and Formal Defusing

The process of defusing as outlined by Jeffrey Mitchell is confined to helping *after* a traumatic event, although it can be
extended to include what happens before and during it. Using
the analogy of defusing a bomb, it is necessary to know what to
do on the spot, but training, preparation and support before and
after the incident, as well as during it, are essential. This more
inclusive use of the term 'defusing' can be called 'comprehensive
defusing' (see Summary 4), and it can be defined as:

> the process of support mechanisms and procedures before,
> during and immediately after a traumatic incident, the aim of
> which is to provide a positive and supportive atmosphere and
> to re-establish the solidarity of the team or group. (Parkinson
> 1993b)

BEFORE THE INCIDENT

Training
Professional helpers, rescuers and carers need to be trained, and
those who are new or inexperienced can find it more difficult to
cope. Training injects confidence into individuals and groups,
builds up solidarity, team spirit and morale, and enables people to
cope and perform their duties efficiently and effectively without
allowing their reactions to disable them.

However, this same professionalism can result in a strengthening of defences, produce a powerful macho response, and lead
to a denial of feelings or reactions. Defusing procedures and
Critical Incident Debriefings aim to help people to acknowledge

Summary 4: The comprehensive defusing model

Before the incident	*Training*	For professionals.
	Education	Coping strategies.
		Post-traumatic stress reactions.
		Defusing and Debriefing procedures.
	Preparation	Factual information.
		Emotional preparation.
During the incident		Importance of presence of senior personnel at early stage.
		Need for good communications.
		Personal contact.
		Rest periods.
		Should welfare and support personnel be present?
		Media involvement.
		On-going involvement of rescuers and helpers.
After the incident		*Operational Debriefing:* practical issues.
		Simple defusing.
		Peer supporters and future help.
		Formal defusing.
Decide:		Is a Critical Incident Debriefing necessary?

and deal with their real reactions and break through these defences.

Supervision, guidance and support should also be provided for any who may be helping at the scene of an incident but who are *untrained*, such as witnesses or bystanders who have perhaps rushed in to offer assistance. Amateur helpers might well go home once the incident is over, completely unaware of what may be happening to them in terms of stress, or of what might happen later, and of the effect this might have on them and their families. It is useful to take the names and addresses of any such people so that, if necessary, a follow-up can be done by social services or welfare personnel. This would be especially appropriate at a major disaster.

Education

The education and training of professionals should include awareness of:

1 Coping strategies.
2 Post-traumatic stress reactions.
3 Defusing and Debriefing procedures.

This applies not only to new recruits, but to staff at all levels: if senior management are not aware of possible reactions or of the reasons for defusing and Debriefing, they may not provide the necessary training, understanding and support.

1 Coping strategies

Already outlined in Chapter 3, these are particularly important because they maximise natural defence mechanisms and techniques that help individuals and groups to cope, and they can be included in training sessions. There are also strategies for coping with stress that professionals can be taught on stress management courses.

2 Post-traumatic stress reactions

As already mentioned, all personnel at all levels should have some knowledge of the normal psychological and physiological reactions to stress and traumatic incidents, and should be aware of the possible effects on individuals, groups and families and on their health, work and relationships. Training should emphasise that all reactions are normal, and not the result of weakness or incompetence. As well as general reactions, the particular post-traumatic responses of re-experiencing, avoidance behaviour and arousal, discussed in Chapter 2, should be explained.

Some people fear that giving information may have a negative effect and frighten people, or make them feel that they should or will inevitably have the reactions described.

A senior army officer remarked to the person who was to conduct Critical Incident Debriefings with groups of soldiers, 'You are trying to persuade these men that they owe themselves a problem.'

In other words, if you tell people what reactions they *might* have, they will then be predisposed, as with a self-fulfilling prophecy, to experience them. Fear and anxiety may indeed increase, but such an approach denies the humanity, intelligence and integrity of individuals and groups and can result in even stronger defences against admitting to having, and dealing with, reactions. Most people cope better with difficult experiences if they are prepared for them, and professionals should be able to absorb the necessary information, evaluate and assess it, and then use it appropriately. Information also enables them to monitor their own responses and the reactions of others. Defusings and Debriefings do not suggest to the debriefees that they *will* have problems, but deal mainly with what is present in the session.

3   Defusing and Debriefing procedures
It is important that professionals know what procedures will normally be followed during and after an incident. This includes information about rest periods, the provision of refreshments, and awareness of any defusing, Operational Debriefing or Critical Incident Debriefing that may follow. Such advance information ensures that all these aspects are seen as part of what some organisations call SOPs—'standard [or standing] operating procedures'. It normalises such procedures and obviates the need for personnel to ask for help and, by having to do so, perhaps feel incompetent. They should also be aware of any help and support resources provided by the employer organisation: welfare, personnel or human resources departments; occupational health doctors and nurses; counsellors, chaplains and consultant psychologists or psychiatrists; plus any local external agencies offering advice and support such as Victim Support, the Samaritans, Cruse, Relate and the Compassionate Friends.

Preparation
This is the preparation made by personnel when they have been informed of an incident and are on their way to it.

Factual information
As much information as possible should be given beforehand about who is involved and what kind of incident it is.

- Is it a fire or a traffic accident, suicide, murder or rape?
- Does it include vehicles, aircraft or buildings?
- Does it involve people—adults, children, young people—or animals?
- Where has it happened? Outside? In a building, a wood, a town centre?
- What are they likely to find at the scene?
- Will other rescuers and helpers be present?

Informative answers to these questions will enable them to form ideas of what the incident might involve and, as well as telling them what equipment they will need, will help them to prepare emotionally.

Emotional preparation
When given information, people will begin to filter it through their personal and professional experiences and ask themselves questions:

'This is my first experience of an incident of this kind—what will it be like and how will I cope?'
'Have I attended similar incidents?' 'Will this be easier or worse?'
'What can I expect to find when I arrive at the scene?'
'How did I cope last time I attended a similar incident, and how did it affect me at the time and later?'
'Will I be able to cope with the dead or injured, especially if there are children?'

Someone who has experienced or is experiencing another incident involving loss or change in their lives, such as a divorce, personal problems or a bereavement, may find it more difficult to cope than those who are not.

Once information has been received, there will probably be a rise in individual and group confidence, with much talking and interreaction. Adrenalin will flow, and anticipation and excitement may be evident. But people's responses will depend to some extent on the nature of the incident as well as on the information that they have been given before they arrive. Foreknowledge of some incidents, especially of major disasters or of those involving children, may produce silence and anxiety.

DURING THE INCIDENT

During the incident employer organisations should ensure that certain criteria are met which will help people to cope.

Senior personnel

Senior personnel should be present and visible at the scene as early as possible. If they arrive later, their intervention may be seen as intrusive and cause anger and resentment. After a fatal traffic accident police officers said of a senior officer:

> 'We have been coping and were here at the beginning. Suddenly he comes along and starts telling us what to do. Who does he think he is? If he cared, he would have been here earlier.'

This is a reaction often exacerbated by shock and natural defences. So senior personnel need to be sensitive to the possibility of such responses at the scene. It is common for professionals to feel anger about what has happened and to project it onto the organisation in some way.

Avoiding isolation

Where possible, neither groups nor individuals should be isolated. Some may already feel isolated because of their own previous or present experiences and the defences they are using. Junior or inexperienced personnel should be with more experienced colleagues, or they can feel alone, de-skilled and ineffective.

Promoting communications

Good communications between people are essential: they can prevent isolation and reinforce group solidarity. Information about what is happening will probably be exchanged at a personal level, and this can increase confidence. But some will cope by concentrating on the tasks in hand and will be unwilling to hear about what may be taking place elsewhere.

Personal contact

There will probably be much touching and talking amongst some personnel as a means of receiving and giving support, while others will wish to be left alone to carry on with their work, and will avoid such contact.

Rest periods

There should be opportunities for rest, and hot drinks and snacks should be provided. The length and frequency of rest periods will depend on the length and intensity of the incident, but they should not be too long—otherwise, rescue workers may find it difficult to return to work. Breaks provide an opportunity for people to talk and relax. Some, anxious to get back to work, will find this difficult to do. But rest periods can be essential for their survival and their ability to carry on.

Other personnel

Welfare and support personnel can be at the site and available to talk informally with rescue workers, but only at the wish of those involved. With incidents that stretch over a long period, a room, caravan or other 'headquarters' can be set up, where people can speak to welfare officers, chaplains, counsellors, psychologists and others in private. However, welfare personnel should be reactive, not proactive, during the incident. Being present at the site will familiarise them with the nature and extent of the incident and advertise their availability, but they must not intrude or interfere.

People do not usually need or ask for counselling during or immediately after an incident. As a general rule, people should not be asked 'How do you feel?'—such an approach can result in anger and resentment and a strengthening of defences. At this stage feelings are usually suppressed. People need familiar faces around them, not strangers who may be seen as threatening and intrusive. Immediate victims need their colleagues, friends and families, and these need information about what is happening, why the incident happened and what is being done.

The media
Media involvement must not be intrusive, and a press officer should be appointed to deal with inquiries. Giving information to the public and to the press can be important, but victims, helpers and rescue workers alike are often vulnerable and may agree to say and do things they will later regret. Sometimes victims, helpers or relatives are asked by the media for comments when they are in no fit state to be interviewed. Such intrusion may deepen defences and delay natural healing processes. However, sensitive media involvement can be helpful in showing that others do care and in allowing people to express their feelings, as well as stimulating positive reactions from organisations or governments.

On-going involvement
Where possible, rescuers and helpers should be allowed to stay at the scene until the incident is over. Changes of individuals or teams may cause adverse reactions:

'We should have been there throughout. After all, we were there at the beginning, so why did others come and take over?'

When they have to be moved because of operational commitments or exhaustion, the initial team should be kept informed about what is happening and be involved in any subsequent demobilisation, Operational Debriefing, defusing meeting or Critical Incident Debriefing. And where necessary, follow-up contact should be made—by colleagues as well as by welfare personnel. For example, an officer who is injured at a scene and sent home or to hospital may consider that his task was unfinished and feel regret, anger, failure or guilt: he should be informed about what happened after he left and be involved in defusing or Debriefing.

AFTER THE INCIDENT

Operational Debriefing

As already mentioned, Operational Debriefing is normal procedure in many organisations, such as the police and military. Usually led by a senior officer, it is held as soon as possible after the incident. The object is to look at what happened, at how they responded as an organisation and as groups within it, and at what can be learned for the future. It rarely involves considering emotional reactions, but can be used to determine whether or not a Critical Incident Debriefing is necessary.

Defusing

Whether or not an operational Debriefing is held, after the incident a *simple* or *formal defusing* meeting should be organised. It should be immediate, be held in a suitable environment and involve everyone; and it should be informal.

- *Immediate* It should take place as soon as the incident is over, and either before or after an Operational Debriefing.
- *In a suitable environment* It can be held on site—which will confirm the reality of both the incident and everyone's involvement. Mitchell, though, advises that defusings be held in a neutral environment, away from the site, so that those involved can begin the process of moving back into their normal world. Both venues have potential benefits.

- *Involve everyone* All personnel at the scene of an incident can attend a defusing, no matter what their role. However many there are, they should all be able to see and hear everyone else and feel involved. With large groups more than one defusing may be conducted, although there are benefits to be derived from gathering everyone together. After armed robberies, accidents, suicides or violence in work premises, for instance, all members of the team or group should be present, whether involved directly in the incident or not. But any who did not take part and do not belong to the group or team should not attend, as their presence may be threatening and result in a reduced willingness to talk or share experiences.
- *Informal* Although it has a structure, a defusing meeting should usually be informal and flexible. Even a formal defusing should preserve an air of *in*formality, while maintaining feelings of confidentiality and safety. No outsiders or observers should be present. It may need to be in a room, but can equally be held outside with everyone gathered round.

Simple defusing

At a conference in Bergen in 1992 it was claimed that research in the USA showed that over 60 per cent of police officers reported that when they returned to their duty station nobody mentioned the incident to them, least of all their senior officers. Nobody asked them what had happened, how they had coped or how they were feeling. This, if true—if it is not just a perceived lack of response—is bad management, and those in charge were not fulfilling their responsibilities for the welfare of their officers.

Simple defusing (Summary 5) can be done with individuals and groups, either immediately following an incident or just before they go off duty. It should take place in a safe and confidential environment, people should be made comfortable and refreshments provided. The meeting should take from ten to twenty minutes. A police officer involved in a traumatic incident should have a simple defusing when the incident is over. It should include allowing him to rest for a short while, have a hot drink

Summary 5: Simple defusing

	Time 10–20 mins
Venue	Defuser provides a safe and confidential environment.
	Makes sure that people are comfortable.
	Provides refreshments.
Introduction	Defuser suggests that it will help to talk.
	Is sympathetic.
	Allows people time to relax.
Facts	'Where were you before, during and after the incident?'
	'What happened?'
	'What did you do?'
Feelings	'How did you react?'
	'How did you feel at the time?'
	'How did you feel later, when it was over?'
	'How were you treated by those present?'
Future	'How are you now?'
	Defuser reassures defusees about the normality of their reactions.
	'What do you feel you need—if anything?'
	'Are you ready to go back on/off duty?'

and talk, if he wants to. He should be expected, and encouraged, to then go back on or off duty. Many military and emergency services personnel automatically do this at junior level. Fire and rescue officers usually go back to the watch-room, where they relax and talk, sometimes with a senior officer, chaplain or welfare officer offering support and encouragement. The problems presented by the common use of black humour are discussed in Chapter 3.

Simple defusing does not always follow an obviously structured pattern.

After an armed robbery in a bank, members of staff were badly shaken. The manager took charge of the situation immediately the robber left, closed the branch and ensured that all members of staff were able to rest and given a hot drink. Within a short while, twelve police officers arrived.

From her experience of a previous raid where the same thing had happened, the manager knew that staff members had felt angry and threatened because the robber had taken away their control, and that the subsequent invasion of police officers had produced the same reactions in them. So she asked the senior officer to send away any officers who were not needed, and refused to let them take any of the staff members to the local police station to give statements, insisting that these be taken at the branch. She felt that for mutual support they had to stay together as a team, and that taking some away would disrupt the group and make it difficult for them to return to the branch.

The police investigations were concluded by mid-afternoon, and the manager decided to keep the branch closed and allow staff to go home. Before she did this, she gathered them all together for half an hour and invited them to talk about what had happened and how they felt about it. She knew that one young woman lived alone in a flat and that another would be on her own until her husband arrived home later that evening. She arranged for other members of staff to accompany them home and stay with them; the young woman on her own had a friend from the branch stay with her overnight. They all returned to work the next day and, although some were still upset and nervous, they coped. A Critical Incident Debriefing took place two days later.

This was an excellent example, not only of leadership and good management, but also of simple defusing.

Senior officers, managers and supervisors can conduct simple defusings, making time to ask those for whom they are responsible about the traumatic incident in question. The individual or group should be invited to sit down; then, questions such as these can be asked:

'Where were you and what were you doing before the incident happened?'
'How did you hear about the incident?' 'How did you get involved?'

'What happened, and what did you think about it?'
'What did you do?'
'How did you react at the time, and when it was over?'
'How do you feel now?' 'Do you need any further help?'
'Are you ready to go on/off duty?'

The defuser should also assess the possible need for a formal defusing or Critical Incident Debriefing.

Simple defusing is like a mini-Critical Incident Debriefing.

Peer supporters and future help
Some organisations have specially trained personnel, usually called peer supporters or peer counsellors, who make it their job to be available for or to seek out those who have experienced traumatic incidents. Some are reactive and others proactive: the proactive approach is probably more effective, because most people will not ask for help. Peer supporters are trained in basic listening skills, to understand traumatic reactions and to offer support and referral. They can conduct simple defusing and act as helpers during and after longer defusing meetings or Critical Incident Debriefings.

Formal defusing
Formal defusing is more structured than simple defusing; the defuser should:

- Ask about participants' reactions.
- Comment positively about their performance.
- Not allow undue criticism.
- Attempt to reduce excessive black humour.
- Be aware of defence mechanisms.
- Mention that a Critical Incident Debriefing might follow.

Formal defusing does not go into as much detail, or as deeply into feelings and emotions, as Critical Incident Debriefing, and should take from thirty minutes to an hour. As in the Mitchell model of defusing, if the level of reactions is high and the session is prolonged, the defuser may decide that a Critical Incident Debriefing is needed later.

The following points are important:

● *Excluding destructive criticism* Some will wish to criticise organisations or individuals and look for something or someone to blame. Criticism, whether deserved or resulting from reactions to the trauma, is sometimes expressed; but it should be kept to a minimum. And least of all should people be allowed, at this stage, to focus their criticisms or feelings on other members of the team. Such unleashings can result in many negative reactions, which can increase defences against expressing feelings and make some feel angry, guilty or bitter. Where there has been actual failure it can be mentioned, but no attempt should be made either to justify or condemn it.

● *Discouraging excessive black humour* Black or sick humour, as we saw in Chapter 3, is a common mechanism for coping with horrific incidents. But it should be discouraged because it may cause real feelings to be suppressed and entrench defences even deeper.

● *Being aware of macho defences* Some, via silence, aggression or false bravado, will refuse to tell their stories or to express their feelings. It can be helpful to mention the ways in which defences operate and to talk of the positive benefits of letting feelings out rather than keeping them buried inside. The defuser might decide to speak to people behaving in this way after the defusing.

● *Choosing the right venue* As with simple defusing and Debriefing, the meeting should take place in a safe and confidential environment, whether at the scene of the incident or somewhere else. People should be made comfortable and refreshments provided.

The *structure* of the formal defusing (see Summary 6) is similar to that of the models for Critical Incident Debriefing.

● Introduction
● Facts and reactions (cognitive mode)

Summary 6: Formal defusing

	Time 30 mins–1 hour
Venue	Defuser provides a safe and confidential environment.
	Makes sure that people are comfortable.
	Provides refreshments.
Introduction	Defuser explains the aims:
	• To reduce the level of reactions.
	• To share reactions, experiences and feelings.
	• To reassure that reactions are normal.
	• To re-establish group or team solidarity.
	• To give information about the incident.
	• To provide support.
	• To provide information about any future reactions.
	• To prepare for a return to normality.
Facts and reactions	'What were you doing before the incident?'
	'What happened, and how did you react?'
	'What did you do?'
Emotions and feelings	'How did you feel at the time?'
	'How did you feel later, when it was over?'
	'How were you treated by those present?'
	'How do you feel now?'
Information	Defuser gives information, particularly about possible reactions.
	'What do you feel you need—if anything?'
Re-entry	'Are you ready to go back on/off duty?'
Decide:	Is a Critical Incident Debriefing necessary?

• Emotions and feelings (emotional mode)
• Giving information (cognitive mode)
• Re-entry.

Introduction
The defuser introduces himself and explains the aims of the
meeting, which are similar to those for Critical Incident
Debriefing: to reduce the level of reactions; to normalise reactions; to re-establish team solidarity; to give information about
the incident; to provide support and reassurance; to prepare for
a return to normality and allow the opportunity for questions.
The defusing also enables the defuser to decide whether or not
a Critical Incident Debriefing is necessary.

Facts and reactions
People are invited to tell their stories and explore what happened
and what their reactions were. Questions such as these can be
asked:

'What were you doing before the incident happened?'
'How did you become involved?'
'What did you expect, what happened, and what did you do?'
'What happened when the incident was over?'

Emotions and feelings
The defuser asks such questions as:

'How did you feel before, during and after the incident?'
'How do you feel now?'

Giving information
The defuser gives information about the incident, about why it
happened, about whether there were casualties, and about how
successful they, the rescue personnel, were. He tells them that
reactions may take place later—when they have gone home, the
next day or when they return to work—and stresses that these
are normal and natural and not signs of weakness. Where there
is evidence of distress, no attempt should be made to counsel or
to delve into feelings or focus on particular individuals. The
defuser should make positive comments about the performance
of personnel; and where there have been casualties or deaths,

especially of colleagues, he should express sorrow and regret. Where there are feelings of failure, guilt or horror, the defuser should balance out the positive and negative elements of involvement in the incident in order to show that people did what they could and that they did their best.

● *Support and future meetings* The defuser should inform people about the availability of support through both in-house and external agencies. Where appropriate, he should let them know that there will be an Operational Debriefing to look at practical issues and that, if considered necessary, a Critical Incident Debriefing will be held for everyone in a few days' time to look at the incident in more detail.

● *Any questions?* After asking whether there are any comments or questions, the defuser should conclude the meeting by saying that he will be available should anyone wish to talk further. He should make sure that he is aware of any who might need follow-up or referral and, where necessary, take action to provide it.

Re-entry

When the meeting is over, everyone should normally return to duty. However, in some cases—for example, after a serious incident involving excessive use of violence, or where there is injury, death or severe traumatisation—it may be felt that those involved should be sent home. Police inquiries and forensic investigations may also call for a place of work to close; this can also happen because their work has finished, but for most incidents it is not good practice. Those involved will cope better if they are not treated as though they are ill. Unless they need medical help or are very distressed, taking time off for rest, a hot drink and a snack may be all that is needed. As always, managers and other senior personnel will need to be sensitive to people's reactions and take decisions appropriate to the situation.

Following an armed robbery one morning in a building society office, the staff thought that when the police had left at lunch-time they themselves should have been sent home. But the manager felt that this was inappropriate and inadvisable: he re-opened the branch and kept the staff at work. They had all coped well, nobody had been injured and there were no overt adverse reactions; he felt that had they gone home they might have found it more difficult to return to work the next day.

Asking for or giving time off can be an attempt to avoid the situation and the feelings generated, and if such avoidance is prolonged, feelings and reactions may not be acknowledged. But with major incidents, where someone is severely injured or killed, non-professional staff should not be expected to carry on as normal. Families of victims may need to be visited, informed and comforted.

When the defusing is over, people may be so exhausted that it might be more appropriate to allow them to go home rather than to offer them refreshments. The defuser will need to make an on-the-spot judgement about this, and about how to end the meeting.

If it is decided to hold a Critical Incident Debriefing, it should be mentioned and, if necessary, the aims and procedure explained.

7 Critical Incident Debriefing: Preparation and Training

Before outlining the revised Debriefing model in detail we must consider two questions:

1 When should Debriefing be used, and with whom?
2 What qualifications should a debriefer have?

1 WHEN SHOULD CRITICAL INCIDENT DEBRIEFING BE USED AND WITH WHOM?

Which incidents?

Critical Incident Debriefing is structured to reduce the level of possible psychological, emotional and physical reactions to a traumatic event. It can be used with groups or individuals after any traumatic incidents in which acute distress, shock, horror or violence are present, such as:

- Natural and man-made disasters.
- Car crashes and other traffic accidents.
- Shootings and bombings.
- Rape, muggings and other kinds of personal assault.
- Armed robberies and hostage situations.
- Suicides, murders and other violent deaths.
- Accidents at work and at home.
- Experiences of overseas aid workers.
- Experience of war and combat.
- Non-successful rescue attempts.
- Burglary and robberies in the home.
- Deaths, especially of young people, children or babies.
- Redundancy and retirement.
- Hysterectomy and abortion.

With whom?
As well as with the immediate victims, Debriefings may be held with:

- Police, fire and rescue and ambulance service personnel.
- Members of the Armed Forces.
- Doctors, other medical staff, social workers, welfare personnel.
- Aid-agency workers, overseas and on their return.
- Bank and building society staff.
- Witnesses, bystanders and non-professional rescuers or helpers.
- Non-injured survivors.
- Relatives, colleagues and friends of victims.

Add to these: postal workers, bus drivers, lorry drivers, housing department staff, shop assistants, and others who have been mugged, robbed, or otherwise assaulted or abused in the course of their duties; those who deal with cases of child abuse and marital or family violence; those to whom the news has just been broken that they have a serious illness or are about to lose their eyesight or a limb; those who have been physically or sexually abused.

Young people and children
Debriefing can be used with young people, although some will find the procedure difficult. While the cognitive–emotive structure will be maintained as far as possible, the Debriefing may need to be flexible and allow more emotions to emerge in the early stages than would perhaps be usual. Children below a certain age, probably about eight, may be unable to verbalise their feelings or talk about the incident in a way that separates the facts from the feelings. This depends, of course, on the development and ability of the particular child or children. Some therapists specialise in art therapy with young children, encouraging them to make drawings and paintings of their experiences. Others use play therapy with dolls, toys and models.

The two-day rule

Critical Incident Debriefing should not take place until 36–48 hours have elapsed after the incident. If an incident happens on a Monday morning the Debriefing should not take place until the Wednesday or Thursday, at the earliest. As mentioned earlier, those involved in an incident are usually in a state of shock, with defences operating at full strength to enable them to cope. People are often unable or unwilling, at the early stage, to talk in any great detail about the incident and, when they do open up, what they say is almost always unstructured and usually confused.

After armed robberies, building society staff usually return to work the next day; many say that they feel mentally and physically 'numb, confused and jumbled up inside'. They carry on with their work, occasionally talking to others about the incident, but not in any great detail. Some find it difficult to recall what happened at work the next day, except to say that although they did not make any mistakes they felt like robots operating on automatic pilot. Usually, by day three, most will agree to attend a Debriefing and feel that they can begin to talk about their experiences and reactions.

At a conference in Norway in June 1993 Jeffrey Mitchell said that, although memories of an incident may be influenced by subsequent thoughts and experiences, the model can be used up to eight weeks after the event. And, as already mentioned, it can sometimes be used much later. Soldiers, traffic accident victims and others have been encouraged to talk years after the experience, using the Facts–Feelings–Future cognitive approach. In some cases this Debriefing has been used within on-going counselling (discussed in Chapter 14).

Is a Debriefing needed?

When determining whether a Debriefing is appropriate, the following criteria should be considered:

1 The timing of the incident.
2 The nature of the incident.
3 The characters and previous experiences of those involved.

4 The support given at the time and later.

These are the same criteria that can indicate how a person may react to traumatic events. They can point to increased vulnerability, leading to a strengthening and hardening of defences, or a willingness to talk about reactions and to express feelings.

1 Timing of the incident
There are certain times when an individual or group may be especially vulnerable to traumatic reactions.

● *When did the incident take place?* Early in the day, when people may be more alert? Or later when they are tired or about to go off duty, or when they are due to go on holiday or are approaching a weekend break?

● *Is this one of a series of difficult incidents?* There can be the cumulative effect of stress building up over a long period and reaching a crisis point, especially with doctors and nurses, police, fire and rescue and ambulance service personnel.

● *Are other traumatic incidents and reactions happening at the same time?* Is this person (or group) particularly vulnerable because she has recently experienced or is experiencing a family bereavement or the death of a colleague, a divorce or other marital problems, actual or threatened redundancy, lack of promotion, illness, or some other major change or loss?

2 Nature of the incident
As already noted, in general, the more serious the incident, the more extreme the reactions may be.

● *Is this a new experience for those involved?* Those who are used to major incidents may feel disillusioned, angry or a failure when they react intensely to apparently minor events. Also, if earlier, familiar coping strategies are found to be ineffective or inappropriate in dealing with a new experience, disorientation and confusion can result.

● *Was there a high degree of aggression or violence?* This is the case with many traumatic incidents, but especially with experiences such as combat, rape, assault, mugging, hostage situations and riots.

● *Did it last a long or a short time?* A short, violent incident can sometimes generate a much stronger traumatic response than one that is long and only mildly disturbing. However, the opposite can also be true.

● *Was the incident life-threatening?* How serious was the threat to them or to their colleagues, or to members of their families or to friends?

● *Were there deaths of children or young people?* Professionals say that facing the deaths of children and young people is particularly distressing.

● *Was the incident sudden and unexpected?* If so, both during and after the incident, reactions of shock, horror or fear can be at a high level, and people may be more defensive.

An affirmative answer to any of these questions signals the likelihood of overt reactions such as anger, panic and distress. Or feelings may be suppressed, resulting in silence or resentment.

3   Characters and previous experiences of those involved
Character and personality are factors that make some individuals and groups more vulnerable than others, especially if they have recently experienced, or are experiencing, other problems.

● *Does this incident follow a major life-change for anyone involved?* Already discussed under (1) above, this question must also focus on other critical experiences, including demotion, the birth of a baby; an adverse report at work, or disciplinary action; involvement in an accident; expected retirement; a hysterectomy; a mid-life crisis.

● *Have there been recent major changes in the employer organisation?* Changes in leadership, in rules, in equipment or in methods of operating, for instance, can affect individual and group morale and confidence.

● *Have those involved recently experienced psychological or physical distress?* Illness, hospitalisation, depression or bouts of anxiety, irritability or other signs of increased vulnerability— all of these, whether in the individuals concerned or in their families, may also influence reactions.

● *Is there a history of difficulties with this person, team or group?* Are there already tensions in the group? How do the individuals in it relate, and are there any who are new, who have difficulty in fitting in, or who are disliked or distrusted by others? Has someone been behaving in a manner that is out of character?

● *How macho is this person or team?* Macho self-images can increase confidence, but they can also lead to over-confidence or give the impression that people are coping when they are not.

Managers and other senior staff must know the individuals and groups for whom they are responsible and be aware of the pressures they are under both at work and at home.

4 Support given at the time and later
Managers need to know who was involved in the incident, what support they were given, and what happened when it was over.

● *Was this an incident in which an individual was alone or isolated?* Isolation can increase or decrease the ability to cope: it may strengthen defences, or it may erode them and lead to anger, bitterness or a sense of failure, or a feeling of having been let down by the organisation or by colleagues.

● *How were those involved treated by others?* This includes treatment by colleagues, seniors, those from other groups or organisations, civilians, rioters, the media, criminals, suspects and victims. Were those involved ignored, verbally abused or physically assaulted?

● *Were there opportunities for rest, and were refreshments available?* If not, fatigue or exhaustion may have been experienced, which can lower coping mechanisms and result in stronger reactions either at the time or later.

• *Were peer supporters or welfare personnel available, or involved?* If peer supporters, counsellors, psychologists or others have been present to offer help, managers and other senior personnel may know which individuals have asked for or been given support; on the other hand, such information may be confidential. Welfare involvement may lead to better coping, although some may resent it, especially if such involvement has been perceived as insensitive or intrusive.

• *Was there an Operational Debriefing or a defusing meeting?* If so, was it conducted by properly trained personnel, and have there been any reactions or responses? Some may be rather annoyed, even angered, by these procedures. It may be necessary to contact those who conducted any Operational Debriefing or defusing meetings to ask advice about holding a Critical Incident Debriefing. Defusing may reduce the need for one, or may suggest that one is called for.

• *How did this person or group react to the incident, and how are they reacting now?* As already pointed out, external appearances do not necessarily show how people are coping. Some may be visibly distressed—shaking, aggressive, resentful, angry or upset; others may be sad, surly or silent.

None of the pointers listed above necessarily offers a reliable indication of how people are reacting, or may react later; nonetheless, they should help senior staff to decide whether or not to hold a Critical Incident Debriefing. For example, when a police officer has experienced a difficult incident his sergeant or inspector should conduct a simple defusing. He should take into account the nature of the incident, what happened, his personal knowledge of the officer and how he is reacting and coping. This should enable him to decide whether a formal defusing or a Critical Incident Debriefing is necessary, or whether to seek advice. If in doubt, at least an informal defusing should be organised. Although an individual or group may seem to be coping well at the time, they may later show signs that suggest the need for a Debriefing.

2   WHAT QUALIFICATIONS SHOULD A DEBRIEFER HAVE?

Who should be debriefers?

Mitchell's organisation in the USA requires Debriefings to be led by 'mental health professionals' assisted by specially trained peer supporters. Although it is not the intention, this can suggest that Debriefing should come under the umbrella of the medical profession and that reactions are therefore medical in origin. There are good reasons for having mental health professionals in charge:

- They are used to dealing with people under stress.
- They are familiar with confidentiality.
- They may be trained in counselling techniques.
- They are unlikely to be viewed as a threat because they are professionals and, probably, outside the employer organisational structure.
- They bring with them already established professional authority and standing.
- They are usually insured against litigation.

Of course, these criteria may equally apply to many other professionals. In Scandinavia and other parts of Europe, for example, there are teams of trained personnel who can be called upon to conduct Debriefing sessions: drawn from a wide range of professions, they comprise mainly counsellors, psychotherapists, psychologists, psychiatrists, welfare officers, doctors, occupational health nurses, clergy and police officers. The key to the success of such teams is selection and training, followed by on-going personal and group support; points 1 to 12 cover the main requirements.

1 Selection

Prospective Debriefers should be selected according to the following criteria:

- They should have no overt or covert major problems, nor should they be experiencing, or have recently experienced, a major life change or event. Any 'hidden agenda' can influence the way they conduct and react to debriefees and to the Debriefing.
- They should be empathic rather than sympathetic, and be able to cope with large amounts of emotion both in others and in themselves.
- They should be non-judgemental: being able to accept people without criticism is important.
- They should possess a self-awareness and a confidence that enable them to relate to others as real people, and not hide behind a role or uniform, a pose or position.

2 Basic skills

The skills that a debriefer needs in order to successfully conduct a Debriefing are similar to those required in counsellors:

- *The ability to use basic listening and responding skills* The core skills are those of mirroring (see page 165), paraphrasing, reflecting feelings, summarising what the debriefee has said, and asking questions. The debriefer explores, feeds back, affirms and confirms what is said and expressed.

- *The ability to think laterally* An ability to ask questions in order to slow the story down and probe into descriptions and answers is essential. Debriefees may try to rush through their story and omit important details, so the debriefer must be able to pay attention to detail and avoid, whenever possible, missing some item, event or experience in the story that may be significant.

- *The ability to control a group* The debriefer should not allow any individual or group to dominate the session or detract from the process of moving through the model. Everyone who wishes to talk should be given the space and opportunity to do so. The structure of the model helps to achieve this.

3 *Knowledge of post-trauma stress and PTSD*
The debriefer should know about the possible effects of PTS and PTSD on individuals and families, and be able to give a short presentation on them within the structure of the model.

4 *Knowledge of coping strategies and techniques*
He should know about the possible causes and effects of stress and of the methods people use in order to cope during and after an incident.

5 *Knowledge of group work*
He needs the experience and knowledge of group dynamics and group work. The problem for some professionals and counsellors is that they have experience of working with individuals and couples, but not with groups. They can find it difficult to control groups and to cope with strong group reactions.

In addition, the debriefer should:

6 *Be under supervision*
There should be both individual and group supervision. In any large organisation there should be someone to arrange Debriefings centrally and ensure that debriefers are supervised. The aim of individual supervision is to ensure that there is an opportunity for the debriefer to off-load, to share any problems that have arisen as a result of the Debriefing. Group supervision is directed towards mutual support, sharing experiences, discussing problems, further training and learning, and maintaining group solidarity and professionalism. A debriefer who works alone should ensure that his personal supervisor knows about the Debriefing procedure and about what he, the debriefer, is doing.

7   Be able to organise a Debriefing
Where Debriefings are conducted for or within an organisation, the debriefer should be able to liaise with members of staff and set up the facilities for a Debriefing.

8   Be trained in using the model
The debriefer should be thoroughly familiar with the Debriefing model and method and have attended an intensive training course, lasting at least two days, which included extensive use of role-play.

9   Be able to stay with the Debriefing model
The debriefer needs to be directive and not move into counselling or therapy. This means staying with the Debriefing structure and being able to acknowledge but to hold any feelings that emerge in the initial stages. Some counsellors and therapists find it difficult to stay within the guidelines of the model or to avoid moving into feelings during the introduction and factual stages. They may also expect, mistakenly, to ask questions about family background and childhood experiences which are not pertinent to the model. Although previous experiences are important, the Debriefing concentrates on the incident and its effects in the here and now. The model requires the debriefer to be firmly and confidently in charge, which is often difficult for counsellors to grasp—some find it difficult to change the way they work. Furthermore, most counsellors and therapists work within a framework of fifty minutes to an hour, whereas a Debriefing can take over three hours.

10   Work under a code of practice
Counsellors and many other professionals already work under codes of ethics and practice, such as those of the British Association for Counselling. The major problem may concern confidentiality. If, during the Debriefing, information is disclosed in cases where the law has been broken or where issues of personal and public safety or security are involved, or where there has been sexual or physical abuse, the information must normally cease

to be confidential. The debriefer has to be clear about this and make a decision over what action to take. Confidentiality is carefully outlined at the beginning of a Debriefing, so debriefees should know where the boundaries lie.

11 Be insured
Most professional therapists have private indemnity insurance as a safeguard against litigation. In the case of debriefers selected and trained within an organisation, it is usually the organisation that bears this responsibility, should problems occur. There may need to be written confirmation of this.

12 Not debrief people for whom he is operationally or organisationally responsible
Managers and other senior personnel should not debrief colleagues or others in the same group, team, branch or department, so as to avoid causing problems over confidentiality or making those involved feel threatened or inhibited.

Training for debriefers
Not all professionals can cope with Debriefing.

Seventy hostages were to be debriefed on their release, and it was decided to divide them into eight groups of eight to ten, with a debriefer and a co-debriefer in each group. The debriefers and co-debriefers included psychiatrists, a clinical psychologist, social workers, clergy and welfare officers—all trained and experienced in counselling. Because of the time factor they had to be trained in the model in one day but it was hoped that, given their experience, this would be sufficient. All went well until they began to look at feelings: two co-debriefers had to leave their groups because they could not cope with the massive amounts of emotion that were emerging. There are a number of possible reasons for this: it was a completely new venture for them, a new experience; they may not have been used to working with groups and dealing with group reactions; the training was probably too short, resulting in a lack of confidence; problems of their own could have exacerbated their reactions; there was not enough time, and the debriefers felt under pressure to work through the procedure. Whatever the reasons, the two co-debriefers had to leave. Fortunately, they were able to offer support to debriefees who had also left their groups.

The selection criteria listed on page 125 should be followed for everyone who wishes to be a debriefer. The length of training will depend on which skills they already have.

The two-day course
Many professionals, as well as having good basic listening and responding skills—even if they are not trained counsellors—will have attended various training courses.

> Amongst a group of police officers and support staff selected for training, one had a masters degree in disaster management plus some basic counselling training; others had either attended listening skills courses or were already undergoing counselling training.

If candidates meet the criteria and already have the skills, training can be carried out in two days. The course will include a short session on PTS reactions, and an outline and explanation of the model and its development. Most of the time will be spent role-playing each stage of the model within an appropriate scenario, with a session at the end on follow-up and referral. The role-plays should be conducted in groups of three or four so that participants gain experience of using the model with groups.

Throughout the course there should be opportunities for trainees to discuss what they are learning, in relation not only to using the model but also to adapting their own skills. At the end of the two-day course some will feel able to conduct sessions on their own, while others will benefit from acting as co-debriefers until they gain the necessary confidence and experience.

A typical two-day course might run as follows:

Day 1

Introduction to the course: expectations and aims.
Session 1   Loss, stress and post-traumatic stress reactions.

Break
Session 2   Background to and outline of the model.
Lunch
Session 3   *Introduction*: aims, rules and procedure.
Break
Session 4   *The Facts Stage*: telling the story.
                 Review of the day.

Day 2

                 Introduction to the day.
Session 5   *The Feelings Stage*: expressing and identifying
                 feelings.
Break
Session 6   *The Feelings Stage* (continued).
Lunch
Session 7   *The Future Stage*: education, normalisation and
                 support.
Break
Session 8   Referral, and using the model in different
                 situations.
                 Review of the course, open forum and any
                 questions.
                 Ending

Some believe that professionals can be trained in a day or even a half-day, but this is not recommended because it does not provide sufficient time to understand the model and to gain experience of using it in role-plays. The course should be long enough for consolidating the skills needed for the model and for assessing how the trainees are coping.

Longer courses
Selected candidates who do not have the necessary listening skills or experience of group work can be trained on a four- or five-day course; this is identical to the two-day course but includes training in group work and basic listening skills appropriate to the model.

Police officers and civilian support staff were selected and trained on five-day courses to conduct Debriefings. They adapted easily to using the model, probably because their training taught them to be directive and they were used to being in charge. They would not be debriefing personnel from their own division or area, or people for whom they were operationally responsible. A code of practice was established whereby if organisational problems over confidentiality and discipline arose, breaching police disciplinary codes of behaviour, or if it emerged that the law had been broken, the debriefer would warn the group or individual concerned and a decision would be made as to whether the Debriefing should end. It was established that the employer organisation would be responsible in cases of litigation against debriefers. Personal and group supervision was provided.

At Bristol University there is a two-part course. Part 1 is a day seminar which gives general information about post-trauma stress and PTSD, outlines the model of Debriefing and gives short role-play demonstrations. Some attend Part 1 of this course not in order to become debriefers, but out of interest or personal involvement in traumatic incidents. Part 2 is exactly the same as the two-day course outlined above; all who attend this two-day course should be experienced counsellors or regularly using basic listening and responding skills in their professional lives. At the end of these two days not all will decide to act as debriefers or use Debriefing in their work. The university also offers a one-day seminar every three months giving group support for trained and practising debriefers.

It is essential that those who conduct Critical Incident Debriefing be selected according to the established criteria, trained as described above, and supported. Without this professional approach and support structure debriefers may cause harm both to themselves and to others.

8   Organising a Debriefing

PREPARATION

Debriefings should be thoroughly planned for by all those involved: the debriefer, those to be debriefed, and those professionally in charge of the debriefees. Where Debriefings create or result in problems it is usually because insufficient effort has been put into the preparation.

What can go wrong?

The debriefer did not prepare, or did not stick to the model
The venue was wrong. The room was too small or too large; the chairs were uncomfortable and there was no table; outsiders could look in and there were interruptions; no coffee or tea was provided.

The debriefer failed to find out the facts about the incident; did not know how many people were involved; forgot to explain that there should be no interruptions; did not have a visible clock or watch; did not spend enough time on the Introduction; moved into counselling mode; allowed some people to dominate the group; let facts and feelings become mixed up; allowed the Debriefing to be too long or too short. There was inadequate follow-up and referral, or none at all; there was insufficient liaison with the employer organisation afterwards.

Those being debriefed had not been prepared
There was uncertainty about what was to happen; they expected to be counselled, and were resistant to the process before it began;

they thought it was going to take only an hour; they expected it to be nothing more than a general chat; they were not told what the aim was or what the procedure would be. As a result of any or all of these factors, they were cynical and disruptive or negative and unresponsive.

The person professionally responsible for the debriefees did not prepare
She was uncertain about what the Debriefing was for; forgot to explain to the team or group beforehand the aim of Debriefing or what the procedure was; failed to give positive encouragement to the group about the Debriefing; did not provide refreshments, before or after as appropriate; failed to insist that the Debriefing should not be interrupted; gave the impression that she thought that because she was in charge she herself did not need to be debriefed; although involved in the incident, did not take part in the Debriefing.

Any of these can result in the Debriefing being ineffective. Both those organisationally in charge and the debriefees may feel that it was a waste of time, and that the debriefer did not know what he was doing. Future Debriefings may be sabotaged on the grounds that they do not work and are badly organised; debriefers may become disillusioned and de-skilled and lose confidence both in themselves and in the Debriefing process.

However, there can be occasions when Debriefings are called for but, because of limited time and other pressures, it is not possible to ensure that every preparation has been made. Disasters by their very nature often entail a hectic aftermath, and carers and helpers sometimes have to do their best under trying circumstances. Jeffrey Mitchell has said that any Debriefing is better than none, but this cannot be an excuse for poor planning or preparation—the 36–48-hour rule should give the necessary time for preparation.

Personnel

In planning and organising a Debriefing and ensuring that it will be effective, there are usually four main people or groups to be considered: the senior person responsible for the debriefees; the debriefees; the Debriefing supervisor; the debriefer.

The senior person

The senior person responsible should be aware of the criteria for deciding whether or not a Debriefing is necessary. She should also know and understand the aims and procedures of the Debriefing process, as well as what is required when organising a Debriefing; and be able to explain these to the people who are to be debriefed. She will be an essential link in conveying to the debriefees the importance and effectiveness of the process. If not involved in the actual Debriefing, she should be aware of the nature of post-traumatic stress reactions, know how the Debriefing will operate, monitor her staff after the Debriefing, and be able to help provide support and referral where necessary.

The debriefees

Although, as already noted, the Debriefing may be with an individual, it is often with a team of professionals, or other people who work together and know each other. The solidarity that can be expected from this can help the Debriefing to work but, on the other hand, it might result in collusion, which can sabotage the process. The subject, or subjects, of the Debriefing may be suspicious of its aims and may, because of their reactions to the incident, be wary of being offered what they may see either as counselling or as a suggestion that they are not coping. So they should be carefully and clearly informed about the aims of the Debriefing, the procedure to be followed and the time it may take. All members of the team, even if they were not present at the incident, should attend the Debriefing. This will confirm and preserve group solidarity through the sharing of experiences, thoughts and feelings. Those not present often feel guilty and excluded from the experience of others.

It is not always possible to debrief a group together, in which case the debriefer may need to conduct a series of Debriefings.

> After an armed robbery in a bank, involving eight members of staff, a debriefer was asked to see individuals on their own because it was not possible to close the branch. But when he explained the importance of a group Debriefing, it was agreed that he should see two groups of four, one in the morning and one in the afternoon. Although this was second-best it was acceptable under the circumstances, and meant that the branch could be kept open by the members of staff not being debriefed.

In another armed robbery case, the manager decided to close the branch for the afternoon so that all could attend the Debriefing together.

> A robbery took place in a shop one Saturday and the Debriefing was arranged for the following Tuesday. Two members of staff who were present at the robbery were due to go on holiday for two weeks on the Monday. It was decided to hold a Debriefing as arranged and then, with the approval of the staff, to have another with everyone present when their two colleagues returned.

If the person to be debriefed is in hospital it may be possible—depending on his health and state of mind—to obtain the permission of medical staff for a Debriefing to take place. On the other hand, since a three-hour Debriefing would almost certainly upset hospital routines, it might be better to wait until he has been discharged. If he has to stay in hospital for some time, arrangements may be made to conduct the Debriefing in the most convenient way that circumstances will allow—for instance, in the hospital, with colleagues present. At the least, a short defusing could take place at the hospital bedside. Similarly, if the potential debriefee is confined to his home, it might be possible to conduct a Debriefing or short defusing there.

A one-to-one Debriefing follows the same procedure as a group Debriefing, beginning with the debriefer ensuring that the person to be debriefed is aware of what is to happen and why.

The Debriefing supervisor

The person who has been appointed to act as the first point of contact within an organisation should give advice as to whether a Debriefing should be held. She will hold a list of experienced debriefers and be able to direct one of them to conduct a Debriefing when required. She will also be responsible for providing on-going training and personal and group support for Debriefing teams within the organisation. The Debriefing supervisor may be a senior welfare or personnel officer, an occupational health nurse, a consultant psychologist or a counsellor, or anyone else with a degree of responsibility and authority in the organisation. Senior personnel will request a Debriefing through her and, if in doubt about the need to hold one, will ask her advice. If the answer is yes, the supervisor will provide a debriefer, who will contact the person professionally responsible for the individual or group to be debriefed, gather information about the incident and plan the Debriefing. When it has been organised and the date and time decided, the debriefer will inform the supervisor.

The debriefer

The debriefer may belong to the organisation or be called in from outside through an agency, consultancy or employee assistance programme which can offer counselling, therapy, advice or support as necessary.

Some debriefers are self-employed and work independently. When contacted by the organisation, they arrange the Debriefing through the local supervisor or senior person responsible. Increasingly, organisations are training their own personnel as an internal resource.

ORGANISING THE DEBRIEFING

Once a Debriefing has been requested, the debriefer should ensure that the following questions are answered and requirements met:

Check-list 1: Organising the Debriefing

Where?	A quiet and confidential venue.
	'Do not disturb' sign on door.
	Large enough, but not too big.
	Comfortable chairs and a table.
	Telephones and answering machines switched off.
	Refreshments provided at beginning?
When?	Not until 36–48 hours after the incident.
	Starting-time convenient to all; clock in room.
	Breaks for lunch, tea, etc.
Who should attend?	Take down names and roles (during the incident) of those attending.
	Everyone involved should be present.
	Is there any team member, not present at the incident, who needs to be invited?
	Were any customers or 'civilians' involved?
	Will the senior person be present?
	Senior person to inform debriefees of aim and procedure.
Observers?	None—unless agreed with debriefees.
A thorough knowledge	What do I know about the event? Level of violence?
	Who was involved? Were weapons used?
	Was anyone injured?
	Do I need a diagram of where it happened?
	What reactions towards police or media?
	Any identity parades, inquiries, inquests or court appearances?
	Prepare an information leaflet.
Ending	Refreshments?

Where?

• Where possible, the Debriefing should take place on neutral ground—for example, in a conference room or office in the workplace. The debriefer needs to ask what messages the venue might convey to the debriefees. To use work premises might be threatening, but it could help to normalise the process and make it seem like part of the organisational procedure. No interruptions should be allowed; if necessary, a notice can be put on the door to that effect. The room should not be too big: it would be uncomfortable and distracting for an individual or small group to be debriefed in a large hall.

• The room should not have clear glass partitions or windows through which outsiders can peer in.

• Telephones and answering machines should be switched off.

• An empty circle can be threatening and make those involved feel as though they are in a therapy session. There should be a table in the centre of the room—either a small coffee table, or a large one that people can sit around, with a bowl of flowers, an ashtray (if mutually agreed) and a box of tissues on it.

• All chairs should be comfortable and identical: the fact that nobody has a special chair helps to create the atmosphere of a shared experience. Resentment and anger can result if some have comfortable arm-chairs while others have only hard plastic ones.

• Where possible, flasks of tea and coffee, so that people can help themselves, and biscuits should be available, but not alcoholic drinks. If flasks are not feasible, refreshments may be provided at the beginning, during any breaks, and when the Debriefing is over.

When?

• The time of the Debriefing—at least 36–48 hours after the incident—should be agreed with the senior person and the individual or group concerned. People's work hours (including finishing times), shifts, and overtime arrangements should be taken into account but, ideally, it should run without any breaks.

It is impossible to say how long any Debriefing will take: the debriefer should keep the session open-ended as the different stages can vary in length, but here are some general guidelines:

Introduction	10–15 minutes	
Factual Stage	1–1¼ hours	
Feelings Stage	1–1½ hours	Average time 3–3½ hours
Future Stage	15–20 minutes	
Ending	5–10 minutes	

Experience shows that both a group Debriefing and an individual Debriefing can take up to four hours. That they usually take the same length of time is probably due to the fact that the debriefer structures the sessions according to time rather than according to the number of debriefees.

Here are three typical timetables as a guide for the debriefer:

1 With two breaks Time: 3½ hours

9.45 a.m.	Debriefing meeting with manager or other senior person.
10 a.m.	Familiarisation if possible with scene of the incident. Checking arrangements and venue.
10.45 a.m.	Introduction, and Factual Stage.
12.30 p.m.	Lunch break (group stay together except for visits to the toilet and for smoking).
1 p.m.	Feelings Stage.
2 p.m.	Tea, toilet and smoking break.
2.15 p.m.	Future Stage, and Ending.
3 p.m.	End of Debriefing.

2 With no breaks Time: 3¼ hours

9 a.m.	Debriefing meeting with manager or other senior person.
9.15 a.m.	Familiarisation if possible with scene of the incident. Checking arrangements and venue.

9.45 a.m.	Introduction, and Factual Stage.
11 a.m.	Feelings Stage.
12.30 p.m.	Future Stage.
1 p.m.	End of Debriefing.

3   With no breaks   Time: 3 hours

12 noon	Debriefer's meeting with manager or other senior person.
12.30 p.m.	Familiarisation if possible with scene of the incident. Checking arrangements and venue.
1 p.m.	Introduction, and Factual Stage.
2.15 p.m.	Feelings Stage.
3.30 p.m.	Future Stage, and Ending.
4 p.m.	End of Debriefing

The experienced debriefer will adjust the timings to suit the time available. It would be unwise to arrange a Debriefing at 4 p.m. if staff finish at five, unless they have agreed to stay until the Debriefing is over. Neither should it start at 11 a.m., then break for lunch in the middle of the Feelings Stage. The Introduction and Factual Stages could be completed before lunch and the Feelings and Future Stages after lunch. Any breaks should be short, and people should stay together during them, because splitting up the group can be disruptive and affect the dynamics of the Debriefing.

In some cases a Debriefing can last much longer than three to four hours. Some may take a whole day—for instance, when dealing with hostages and aid workers returning from overseas, where the Debriefing allows for reunions and the fact that stories may be long and detailed.

A group of aid workers returned from overseas from a conflict situation which had developed into a major refugee problem. Some had thought they were going to die and had found it difficult to escape from the country, while others had left without much difficulty. Because they had not seen each other since the trouble began and did not know whether some colleagues were alive or dead, the Debriefing was organised over a day in a quiet retreat house. A short reunion took place in the morning, when there was much hugging and crying. The Introduction and Factual Stage were held before lunch so that stories could be told, and the Feelings Stage followed after lunch. After a short tea break, the day finished with the Future Stage and the Ending. The whole event was planned to be as relaxed as possible and to allow time for people to meet each other informally outside the Debriefing.

The Debriefing described here was open-ended and long, but the debriefer should always keep a careful check on time. During a long Debriefing, especially if there are no breaks, those involved, including the debriefer, may find it difficult to concentrate and become tired, bored or even angry. It is the debriefer's task to gauge the mood and atmosphere of the Debriefing and adjust the time frame accordingly, allowing for breaks where necessary. He should sit where he can see a clock throughout the Debriefing.

Who should attend?
Before the Debriefing, the debriefer should ask who was involved, what their names are, what their roles were during the incident, and whether anyone was injured. He should also ask about the level of violence: were any weapons used? Hand-guns, shot-guns, knives, iron bars, coshes?

The importance of all team members attending has been stressed. But there may be some resistance: when the incident took place, some may have been on their coffee or lunch break, having a day off, on holiday or simply in another room.

Eight members of staff were directly involved in an armed robbery in a building society. Another member of the team had only recently joined, and was working in an office upstairs when the raid took place. She would not take part in the Debriefing, she said, because nobody had been injured, and she could not see the point in having one. There had been a similar robbery in the branch a few months before this young woman had joined the staff. Both the debriefer and the manager tried to encourage her to join the Debriefing, explained its purpose, and emphasised that it was important for the whole team to be debriefed together. But she was adamant, still claiming that it was unnecessary. Another staff member who had been present at the incident was appalled at her attitude: this person, who had experienced the previous robbery, spoke of the disturbing psychological reactions they had all suffered despite the fact that nobody had been physically injured, and of the help that they had received from the Debriefing. The young woman became very angry, and stood her ground. After the Debriefing the debriefer spoke to her, but it was left to the manager to cope with any effects of her refusal, either on her or on the team.

Senior personnel who were not with the team at the time of the incident tend to have very strong feelings of guilt and regret at not having been there to support their colleagues. Others, even if involved in the incident, will not wish to be present at the Debriefing, and there may be a number of reasons for this. They may feel that because they are senior staff they should be strong, not have any reactions, and be able to cope; they may not wish to be put into a position where they risk displaying to juniors what may be seen as signs of weakness; they may feel guilty that they were unable to do anything to prevent the incident; they may be afraid of being criticised; they may feel, since they have to write reports on the incident and on members of staff, that involvement in the Debriefing could be inhibiting and embarrassing both for others and for themselves. Unwillingness to attend can sometimes be a statement about styles of management and relationships with staff, as well as giving information about the senior person's possible feelings and reactions.

It is important that seniors be positive and supportive about the Debriefing, and explain the benefits. It would be unhelpful for a manager to say, for example:

'There will be a Debriefing tomorrow at three o'clock. I don't know what it is about, but you can attend if you want to.'

A more positive way of persuading people to attend would be to explain to staff what the Debriefing involves (even though they may already have been given this information in their training), then make it clear that it is neither counselling nor therapy, and outline the aims. People should not be forced to attend, but it is easier if Debriefings are accepted as normal procedure and written into the organisation's code of practice. It may take some time for this to be accepted, but training, experience and positive attitudes will help. A confidence-inspiring approach might go like this:

> 'We are holding a Critical Incident Debriefing on Wednesday at nine o'clock in the main conference room for all members of the team, and I would like you all to be present to support each other. The aim is to provide an opportunity for you to talk through the incident together and to share experiences. It is being done by a trained debriefer, it isn't counselling, and it will be confidential. You don't have to say anything in the Debriefing, but I would like you to be there. Would you like to ask any questions?'

It is up to the debriefer to check that the facts about the Debriefing have been explained to the debriefees: why they should be there, what will happen, what the aim is and how long the procedure may take. This information will be confirmed in the Debriefing during the Introduction.

Observers?

If anyone asks to sit in as an observer the group's permission should be sought, but as a general rule outsiders should not be present unless they take part fully in the Debriefing, either as members of the group or as co-debriefers.

A regional manager asked if he could attend a group Debriefing as an observer—'I'll just sit at the back and listen'—because, he said, he wanted to see how they were run so that he would have personal experience from which to advise others. The debriefer said that this

was not usual, but that she would ask the group. They replied that
they did not want him present, so the debriefer told the regional
manager, who accepted the group's decision.

An Occupational Health Department doctor who was trained as a
debriefer asked if she could be present at a one-to-one Debriefing.
She was responsible for the debriefee and had referred him for
Debriefing. The debriefer explained to the debriefee that the doctor
was a recently trained debriefer and wished to have experience of a
live session. The debriefee agreed that she should attend, and the
doctor sat behind and to one side of him so that she could not be
seen directly by him.

If outsiders are present, they should be treated as members of
the Debriefing group, sit in the circle with everyone else and, as
appropriate, be asked the same questions as everyone else. They
will be asked where they were when the incident took place, how
they found out about it, how they reacted at the time, what they
did and how it is affecting them now—in other words, the same
questions that the rest of the group are asked.

Co-debriefers

A co-debriefer is someone who has been trained as a debriefer
and who may be either learning from, or taking an active part
in, the Debriefing. At the beginning the debriefer explains what
part the co-debriefer is to play in the Debriefing. The co-debriefer
introduces himself, then chooses one of a number of options:

- To say nothing except to introduce himself and support the
  debriefer by his presence.
- To observe the reactions of the others and, should anyone
  leave, go with him or her to provide support and help.
- To take an active, pre-arranged part in the Debriefing.
- To join in as and when he feels it appropriate, ask questions
  and make comments

If the co-debriefer is to take an active part, he should meet
with the debriefer beforehand to decide who will deal with which

stages. The Debriefing can be divided between them in any way they decide; for example:

Introduction	Debriefer
Factual Stage	Co-debriefer
Feelings Stage	Debriefer
Future Stage	Co-debriefer
Ending	Debriefer

If the co-debriefer joins in occasionally, his questions and comments should indicate that he is not taking over from the debriefer.

Acting as a co-debriefer helps to increase confidence, as well as experience.

A *thorough knowledge of the incident*

It is essential that a debriefer does not go into a Debriefing knowing nothing about the incident. He should speak to the senior person involved, or responsible for those to be debriefed, and ask what happened. If the incident happened in a shop, office, bank, building society, factory, house or other premises he should, if possible, familiarise himself with the place. This may take the form of a guided tour by a senior person or a debriefee, who can tell him where everyone was at the time and explain what happened. A visit to the site may also be useful in enabling the debriefer to familiarise himself with its atmosphere and to understand empathically what the debriefees are talking about.

> In a Debriefing after a hostage situation, the debriefer kept asking questions that angered the debriefees. He had not bothered to find out where they had been held or under what conditions.

The rule is: Never go into a Debriefing cold.

Take, for example, a Debriefing after an *armed robbery*. The debriefer should arrive as early as possible after the incident so that he can tour the premises with someone who can give relevant information such as where everybody was during the incident, what they were doing, where the robber entered, where people moved to, what happened and where it happened, where the security cameras are placed. This will also provide an opportunity to meet members of staff informally. The debriefer should speak to the manager or senior officer, even if she was not present at the incident, to discuss what happened and whether or not she is going to take part in the Debriefing. She may not wish to, but she may need to talk and, possibly, have a mini-Debriefing, which should take place after the main Debriefing. In the case of armed robberies and similar incidents, it is appropriate to explain to any customers or non-members of staff who were present what the Debriefing is about, and ask them whether they would like to join it. However, staff members should be consulted on this point, as they might find their presence threatening, embarrassing or restricting.

After a *traffic accident*, before the Debriefing begins, the debriefer can ask someone to draw a diagram of the spot where the incident took place, showing the layout of the road or junction and where the vehicles and people were before, during and after it; the diagram will prompt a brief description of what happened. A drawing—of a room, house, shop, factory, wood or even a battlefield, for instance—can be useful after many different kinds of incidents where it is not possible to visit the scene.

Major incidents

In the case of a major incident needing more than one debriefer and more than one Debriefing, the debriefers and co-debriefers should meet beforehand to discuss the incident and to organise the Debriefings. Where a large number of people need to be debriefed in separate groups, each group might include, as well as witnesses and onlookers, members of the different professions involved—police and fire officers, ambulance and medical personnel, the military. But this can cause problems over cross-organisational or cultural boundaries, difficulties over con-fidentiality or threats to group solidarity and loyalty. Furthermore, some may simply feel uneasy and unable to talk if police officers or strangers are present. Other factors may cause problems as far as organising help and support is concerned: after the Zeebrugge disaster, victims, survivors and relatives were scattered all over the British Isles, leaving many with only the option of self-referral if they needed help.

Police and media involvement
There are sometimes positive reactions to the involvement of the police, who are usually very sensitive and supportive, but occasionally they make mistakes—sometimes, perhaps, out of over-zealousness.

> After an armed robbery, the police officers who were first on the scene took one young woman witness with them in their car in an attempt to catch the raider. She was shaking with fear, and although it was the middle of December they did not suggest that she take a coat or ask a friend to accompany her. They walked her up and down the platform of the local railway station and even left her alone in the car while they went into a public house. Further increasing her terror, they asked her to look out for the raider, even though he was armed: she thought that she might be killed. Before the Debriefing, she was angry and upset at the way she had been treated.

The press can sometimes be insensitive, too.

> Following an armed raid in a shop, the young woman who had faced the raider found next morning that, without her permission, her name and photograph were on the front page of the local newspaper. She was extremely angry and upset about it, as well as frightened, because she thought that the raider would then be able to identify and victim-ise her.

The debriefer should attempt to discover how those involved have reacted since the incident and how they have been affected by subsequent events.

Taking charge
It is the debriefer's responsibility to ensure that the Debriefing runs as planned and that the aims are achieved. Without careful preparation and planning, Debriefing will not work effectively

and can lead to further problems such as anger, confusion and disorientation in the debriefees and disillusionment with the process and loss of confidence and credibility in the debriefer.

9 The Three-stage Revised Debriefing Model: Introduction

The three-stage revised Debriefing model, outlined briefly at the end of Chapter 5, contains the essential elements and structures of the seven-stage Mitchell and Dyregrov models, condensed for ease of understanding. It begins by encouraging those taking part to talk about their experiences without allowing feelings to emerge and take control. It then moves through the sensory impressions to look at feelings and emotions, and places them very firmly where they belong in the incident. It looks at what reactions emerge in the Debriefing, and how they are affecting people now. The debriefer then talks about the possible effects of traumatic stress, emphasises the normality of the reactions experienced, and looks at support: what personal resources exist within the individual and the group, what is available from the employer organisation, and which external agencies can help?

The explanations and examples given here and in the following chapters are, of course, mine. The reader will need to work out what he or she needs to say and how to say it.

The three main stages are preceded by an Introduction and end with final statements from the debriefees:

Introduction	Purpose, Rules, Procedure.
Facts	Telling the story without feelings.
Feelings	Looking at feelings, emotions and reactions.
Future	Normalisation, Information and Support.
Ending	Final statements.

Note-taking
The debriefer can have his own outline of the Debriefing in front of him to ensure that he stays within the structure and to remind

him of the stages. The main parts can be outlined, as in Appendix A (page 259), or written on small cards with core words and phrases highlighted (see Summary 7).

Some debriefees may expect the debriefer to take notes and make reports on individual members of the group, or that such material will be available to outsiders. Dyregrov suggests that notes can be taken, but only with the agreement of those taking part, and that an outline of the Debriefing be circulated later to the debriefees.

However, as a general rule no notes, reports or recordings should be made during the session, except that the debriefer should write the debriefees' first names on a piece of paper in the order in which they are sitting in the circle. Then, by way of explanation:

Debriefer:	Before we begin the Debriefing I need to say that I have some cards in front of me. These give me a check-list of the procedure that we are to follow. I also have a piece of paper on which, with your permission, I would like to write your first names so that I can use them during the Debriefing. I will not take any notes during the session without asking you first.

The debriefer then begins the *Introduction*, which consists of:

1	Welcome: general matters and self-introduction(s).
2	Explaining the purpose of the Debriefing.
3	Explaining and agreeing the rules.
4	Outlining the procedure to be followed.

The Introduction sets the scene for the Debriefing, establishes the leadership and credentials of the debriefer, and confirms how the session will work. The purpose and aims are explained, the rules laid down and agreed, and the procedure outlined. It also allows the individual or group to settle into their surroundings and become familiar with the rest of the group and with the debriefer. The voice, mannerisms and style of the debriefer begin

Summary 7: The three-stage revised Debriefing model

		Time 3 hours plus
Introduction		Debriefer/co-debriefer introduce themselves.
	Purpose	Debriefer explains the purpose and aim.
	Rules	Explains the rules, agrees them with debriefees.
	Procedure	Outlines the method of working.
1 The facts	*Before*	'What was happening before the incident?'
	During	'What happened during the incident?'
	After	'What happened after the incident?'
2 The feelings	*Sensory impressions*	Sights, sounds, smells, touch, taste.
	Emotions	'What feelings and emotions were generated?' Overt? Covert?
	Reactions	'What physical reactions?' 'What feelings and reactions are present *now*?' 'Any positive reactions?' 'Lessons learned?'
3 The future	*Normalisation*	Debriefer explains that reactions are normal.
	Information	Gives information about possible reactions.
	Support	Personal, group, organisational, external.
	The aftermath	Identity parades, court cases, inquests, inquiries, hospital visits, funerals.
Endings	Final statements. Referrals? Refreshments	

to establish the nature of the relationship which will develop within the group as the Debriefing progresses. The Introduction should not be shortened, unless it is absolutely necessary to do so. Not everything needs to be explained in minute detail, as it is here, but all the essential elements should be included.

Once everyone has arrived they should all be offered a choice of tea or coffee. This should be a brief episode, and people should not be encouraged to talk at length about the incident. The debriefer suggests that all who wish to do so should visit the toilet first, then take their drinks with them into the Debriefing.

The chairs should already be arranged in a circle around a table and the debriefer now establishes where he will sit— with a clock visible. He then asks everyone to sit around the table.

1   WELCOME

Timing and interruptions
The debriefer welcomes everyone and explains that the session will be long—probably three hours or more. No matter how well they have been prepared for the Debriefing, some may still think that they can receive messages or telephone calls from outside. The debriefer reminds them that there should be no such interruptions during the session, and asks that all personal bleepers, bleeping watches and mobile telephones be switched off. It is essential that the flow of the Debriefing is not interrupted. The debriefer lets them know if there is to be a break: if so, it will be short, and not treated as an opportunity to go back to work, even for a short while, because any outside contact may divert attention away from and interfere with the Debriefing process.

Smoking
Some agreement has to be arrived at about smoking. If the Debriefing is to be split into its various stages, the debriefer explains that there will be breaks for those who wish to smoke—

in many organisations, anyway, there is a no-smoking-in-the-building rule.

Self-introduction

The debriefer gives a short outline of his own experience in conducting Debriefings and, if present, the co-debriefer does the same. This should give the group confidence in, and establish the professionalism of, the debriefer and co-debriefer. The debriefer then explains that the Introduction will last about five to ten minutes, and that there will be an opportunity for questions at the end.

2   EXPLAINING THE PURPOSE OF THE DEBRIEFING

The debriefer carefully outlines the aims and purpose of the Debriefing, either working through them separately or covering them all in a general talk. Where possible, he gives specific examples of relevant experiences.

The aims are:

- *To enable those involved to talk through the event*   This allows them to share their own stories and, by doing so, to minimise any disturbing reactions. Talking about experiences and reactions will help, even if it is difficult.

- *To share experiences as a group*   Not everyone will have seen everything that happened; by talking and sharing experiences, they should acquire a more complete picture.

At the moment when an armed robbery took place in a bank, one member of staff was crouching on the floor with her head in a safe. She was told to stay exactly where she was and not to move or look around. She did as she was told, so could only hear what was happening. Because she could see nothing but the inside of the safe, detached sounds, images, thoughts and feelings ranged through her mind. Later, when she listened to others in the Debriefing, she was able to fill in the blanks. By listening to descriptions of the two men, to the details of what happened and to accounts of how others were involved, she was able to make more sense of the incident.

- *To allow ventilation of impressions, reactions and feelings*
There will be an opportunity for those who feel able to do so to
express emotional reactions, from before, during and after the
incident, right up to the present. This may be difficult and painful
for some, but it should help them to feel that such reactions are
not signs of personal inadequacy.

- *To help them to make some sense of the experience*   Traumatic events can cause confusion and anger, and some will ask
questions about what is morally right and wrong and why traumatic things are allowed to happen. The Debriefing should help
to resolve some of the confusion and enable them to make better
sense of what happened and of their own involvement. It will
not necessarily answer all their questions, but should enable them
to put things into a more helpful perspective.

- *To utilise the strengths of the group and to reduce tension*
Sharing and talking within the group should build up group solidarity, demonstrate that some have experienced the same or similar reactions, and help them to discover the kind of support that
they can offer each other.

- *To mobilise resources*   The Debriefing should inform those
involved as to what support is available to them personally and
as a group, from a variety of sources: first, via their own inner
coping methods and mechanisms; then, via family, friends and
colleagues, the organisation for which they work, and outside
agencies.

- *To normalise the situation and their reactions and to encourage them to look to the future*   Some may feel nervous, embar-
rassed or anxious about what they have experienced and are
feeling now, and conclude that they are therefore weak or inadequate. Debriefing emphasises that their reactions are normal.

> After a fatal traffic accident, a young police officer thought that he
> was the only one who felt guilty. The Debriefing revealed to him
> that many others had similar feelings and that his reactions were
> normal.

- *To reaffirm that the Debriefing is not counselling* In spite of what they have been told about Debriefing, some may still think that it is a form of counselling, and this can cause some resistance to the procedure. The debriefer should stress that he is not there to act as a counsellor, but to help them look at the event and its effects on them. If they feel the need for counselling, they can self-refer at any stage in the future.

3 EXPLAINING AND AGREEING THE RULES

The debriefer explains that the Debriefing can only run smoothly if they all work under certain rules, which are for the benefit and protection of all. These rules will need to be negotiated but, in practice, most people readily understand and accept them. They concern the following:

(a) Speaking

Nobody has to answer any questions; if he wants to, the individual can answer some questions and not others. If he does not wish to answer a particular question, he should say so, or hold up a hand or shake his head. This will be respected, and he will not be pressured to reply. All he *will* be asked to say is what his name is and what his role was at the time—but he need not reveal even this if he does not want to.

(b) Confidentiality

All debriefers work under a code of ethics and behaviour, especially as far as confidentiality is concerned, and this needs to be carefully outlined and boundaries made clear. Confidentiality is of special importance to organisations such as the police who, as well as working under the law, have their own codes of practice; they will need to know where they stand with regard to disclosure of information. It is especially important to establish the nature of confidentiality when an investigation, inquiry or court case is pending, and the debriefer should ensure that, whenever possible, statements have already been taken by the police. Where necessary, he should consult someone in authority before the Debriefing about any possible problems over confidentiality and disclosure, and it may follow that some discussion is necessary with the individual or group. The debriefer can make the following points:

● *On group confidentiality*   That nobody should talk to anyone outside the group about what others have said or done or about what has happened during the Debriefing. If it is agreed within the group, they may talk to partners, spouses or anyone else about what they themselves have said or done. What happens in the Debriefing should be for the group only; the debriefer may need to mention his own supervision, but he should make it clear that this does not include mentioning names.

● *On the law and on codes of practice*   That as a general rule, where the law has been broken or there has been criminal activity—for example, sexual abuse of children—confidentiality cannot be offered, but that this will depend on the nature of the information disclosed. If incriminating information is revealed, then the debriefer can say that confidentiality ceases, and what has emerged will need to be discussed and further action decided upon.

Some may remember important details that they have not included in their police statement, and they should be encouraged to hand this on to the police after the Debriefing.

The rules should be discussed so that they can be adjusted, understood and agreed. If the debriefer makes the boundaries of confidentiality clear, those being debriefed should know what they can reveal. Some debriefers may have different rules from others about confidentiality, and these will need to be explained. Some may wish to have them written down so that group members can read and, if necessary, sign them.

The debriefer explains that, if a report has to be submitted to the organisation after the Debriefing, it will not include anything personal about the individuals taking part, but only practical and operational matters which arise in the Debriefing. And these will be mentioned only with the permission of the group.

In the aftermath of an armed robbery at a building society office, members of staff reported that the security camera had appeared to be making a loud clicking noise, which had seemed to anger the robber. They asked if it could be put right, and if they could have security screens and an entrance door controlled by a button from inside. With the group's agreement the debriefer mentioned this to the manager, who had not been present at the Debriefing.

(c) Complaints

People will complain, especially about organisations; but although criticisms of the system or of personnel may arise as a natural part of the procedure, the Debriefing is not a forum for complaints. (Complaints about individuals and conflicts within the group are discussed later.)

(d) Personal matters

If members of the group mention personal problems not related to the event, these will not be dealt with in the Debriefing. If the Debriefing resurrects problems involving previous or current experiences of trauma, they will be briefly acknowledged by the debriefer but not dealt with. The focus of the Debriefing remains that of dealing with the incident and its effects on those involved.

During a Debriefing with an all-male group, one man suddenly said, 'I'm having an affair.' The debriefer acknowledged what he had said, but pointed out that it was not the object of the Debriefing to deal with it. If the man wished to speak to him about it after the Debriefing, he added, he could do so.

A woman in a Debriefing group dealing with an armed robbery suddenly began to cry, recalling her mother's death fourteen months earlier. The debriefer acknowledged it as a difficult and painful event, resurrected by the feelings deriving from the incident and by the Debriefing. He let her cry for a while, paused, and then carried on with the Debriefing by asking her what it was about the incident that had triggered this reaction to her loss. She said it was the fact that she had been afraid during the incident, just as she had when her mother was dying. She realised that the incident had made her more vulnerable and that she had been coping with the loss by burying her feelings. The vulnerability she felt in the Debriefing had allowed these feelings to come to the surface.

When matters other than the main issue arise, the debriefer who is also a trained counsellor might attempt to counsel the individual or group, but this desire to help should be firmly resisted. If necessary, people can self-refer or be referred later. In the case of a previous bereavement, the debriefer notes its importance at the time it is brought up, then mentions organisations such as Cruse and the Compassionate Friends in the Future Stage of the Debriefing.

(e) Feeling worse

The debriefer mentions that some may feel worse during or at the end of the Debriefing, but that this is normal. If anyone cries or shows other signs of being upset, others in the group—a neighbour or friend—will be asked to support him or her. If an individual wishes to leave, he can do so, but someone from the group should go with him and encourage him to return as soon as he feels able to do so.

In a group, the main resource for helping those who are upset is the group itself. With an individual Debriefing, the debriefer can offer support. Any who do feel worse should be reminded that their reactions are natural, but that they might consider speaking to the debriefer later, or seeking other help.

4   OUTLINING THE PROCEDURE

The debriefer explains that the Debriefing will be conducted (a) with the use of questions and (b) by emotional distancing.

(a) Questions

Each person in turn is asked the same questions. Each is allowed to answer as he or she sees fit, without any interruptions from anyone else. Everyone is given his own personal space in which to speak if he wishes to, and moving around the group in order helps to prevent any one individual from dominating. People are asked to speak for themselves and not for others, and it is helpful if answers are personal, using 'I' rather than 'we', 'he', or 'she'; 'I think', 'I feel', 'I saw'—not 'We think', 'He feels', 'She saw'.

Exactly how this is done will vary according to the style of the debriefer. With a group, some will begin on their left or right and move slowly and methodically around the circle. Others will choose to ask different people in turn, ensuring that everyone has an opportunity to respond—here the debriefer needs to keep tight control of who responds and when.

It is better not to ask, 'Who would like to begin?', as it might make some think that they can dominate the group or speak as and when they please. Variation occurs when certain members of the group are the 'main characters' in the incident, with others coming in at a later stage. The debriefer can start by acknowledging the roles of the main characters, and begin with them, bringing in the others as and when appropriate in order to build up the story.

It is useful for the debriefer to point out that, even though some questions may seem inappropriate or even stupid, they need to be asked in order to elicit a response of some kind, even if it is a negative one. Occasionally reactions may be sparked off from one individual to another across the group, but general discussion and cross-group comments should not be encouraged unless they are appropriate and helpful to the Debriefing process.

In a group Debriefing after an armed robbery a young woman who had been in the background during the incident was asked if she had been frightened when the gun was pointed at her. She replied aggressively, 'That's a stupid question. Anybody would be frightened in that situation.' The debriefer did not apologise for the question. When another member of the group who had faced the robber was asked the same question, she said that she had not been frightened at the time but had felt cool and calm, although she didn't know why. Then, when the gunman had gone, she said, she went to the rest-room and began to shake with fear. The first woman looked relieved, saying that she thought that she was the only one who had been afraid, and that she had seen her colleague behave calmly but had not seen her shaking later. The question had been threatening for her—hence her aggressive reply—until she realised that others had similar feelings but reacted in different ways.

Even when the reply is 'No' or there is no reply at all, this response will be respected.

(b) Emotional distancing

The debriefer has to explain that, initially, facts are to be separated from feelings. This can be difficult, and each debriefer must find the method that suits both his own style and the group that he is debriefing; and some debriefees, whether individuals or groups, will find it more problematical than others. But it can be done by creating an image or picture. The following are some of the methods used; each person is asked to tell his story and imagine that:

- He is painting a picture of the incident, like an artist, but is not personally or directly involved.
- He is floating above the incident as if in an out-of-body experience; he can see everything happening and is watching himself from a distance.
- He is making a video or writing a script of the incident.
- He is describing the incident while watching a silent video.
- His feelings are carried by a little child inside him. The child is asked to leave the room and sit on a chair outside the door, and will be called into the room later.
- Each member of the group is carrying pieces from a jigsaw of the incident; they place these on the floor, gradually building up the picture. The feelings and reactions will be identified later, when the jigsaw is complete, then put where they belong in the picture.

They are asked to distance themselves from the event, to push their feelings down inside and control them.

During a Debriefing, the debriefer told the group that at the beginning
he was not going to ask about feelings. 'Thank God for that,' said
one member of the group, 'I'm sick of people asking me how I feel.'

If feelings do emerge during the Factual Stage or earlier, they
should be sensitively acknowledged and affirmed by the debriefer,
and the group should offer support, but the feelings will not be
explored at this stage.

During the Debriefing of a group of police officers after the death
of one of their colleagues, the debriefer began by asking everyone
what he or she was doing before the incident. He had been warned
by the inspector responsible that the sergeant involved was very
aggressive and dominating and would probably try to take over the
session. The first two members of the group replied calmly, but the
sergeant, who was next, immediately began to respond excitedly:
'How do you think I feel? He was one of my men and I was responsible for him.' He became distressed, and began to talk about his
feelings. The debriefer very calmly, but directly, asked him to stop,
saying: 'I appreciate that this is very difficult for you, John, but I
did explain that part of the procedure is to leave feelings out of the
room and just tell the story first, and you did agree to do this. I ask
you to stop for a while and compose yourself and concentrate on
answering the question. [He pauses.] What were you doing before
the incident? We will have an opportunity for you to express how
you feel later. Is that all right?'
     The sergeant was surprised at first, but then apologised to the
group. He took some deep breaths, then calmly answered the question. This did not inhibit him from expressing his feelings later, in
the Feelings Stage, when he became angry and began to cry.

Occasionally someone will ask why the facts and feelings have
to be separated and why he or she cannot tell the story in his or
her own way. The debriefer should explain that the Debriefing
procedure is a form of cognitive restructuring which should help
people to reframe the incident in their minds. It enables them
to remain in control and tell their stories without the feelings
interfering. Trauma often results in confusion, where facts and

feelings are difficult to separate. This process helps to place past and present feelings where they belong in the story. It can also help to identify, within a safe environment, possible triggers for re-experiencing and flash-backs.

> A young woman who had been raped came for a Debriefing. She was firmly convinced that it had been her fault. She gave all the reasons why she was to blame: she should not have been there; she should have been able to prevent it; she should have been able to fight him off; she should not have trusted the man. There was a great deal of anger, but directed entirely at herself. She said that it was not the man's fault, but hers—every feeling she had was due solely to her own stupidity. The debriefer made no comment about all this, but conducted the Debriefing. The young woman managed, with difficulty, to tell the story coldly and calmly, but when the Feelings Stage was reached she became very upset—furious, guilty and help-less. Towards the end of this stage she was saying, 'The bastard, he did this to me.' The Debriefing had enabled her to put things into perspective, to see where her feelings had come from, and to realise that she had not been at fault. It was separating the facts from the feelings that had helped her to do this. The source of the reactions and feelings, although these were most definitely inside her and belonged to her, was what this man had done to her. Later she wrote to the debriefer that this had helped her, and that she had been able to visit the place where she had been raped.

Any questions?
The debriefer asks if anyone has any questions, and tries to answer them appropriately.

Names and roles
The debriefer then asks each person to give his or her first name and to say briefly their role was at the time of the incident. This should not take long—group members should not begin to talk about what happened. Here are two examples of how it might go—the members announce themselves in turn:

1   A Debriefing after a traffic accident

1   'My name is Robert and I am a police officer. My role was to attend the scene of the accident and I arrived later, with Gordon, when the incident was in progress.'
2   'I am Alan Johnston and I am a police traffic officer. With my partner, John Beresford, I arrived first at the scene.'
3   'I am John, and like my partner, Alan, arrived first at the scene.'
4   'My name is Gordon and I am a police sergeant. I am responsible for the traffic team and arrived at the scene with Robert.'

2   A Debriefing after an armed robbery in a bank

1   'I am Sheila and I was standing at the till when the robber came into the branch. I faced him first.'
2   'I am Tracey Smith and I am the deputy-manager. I was making a cup of coffee in the rest room when the robbery took place. I walked into the middle of it.'
3   'Debra Middleton. I was at the second till and I also faced the robber.'
4   'I am Harry Noakes and I was sitting at the desk behind the tills.'
5   'My name is Sharon and I was sitting at the desk in front of the main counter, dealing with a customer.'

The debriefer writes their first names on a piece of paper and asks whether these names can be used during the Debriefing. Nicknames are acceptable unless they are likely to distract people from concentrating on the incident.

   When the Introduction is over, the Debriefer moves on to Stage 1, the Facts.

10   Stage 1: The Facts

The Facts Stage is concerned with building up the story, and concentrates on:

Thoughts	'What were you thinking?'
Actions	'What did you do, and why did you do it?'
Impressions	'What were your impressions?'
Descriptions	Describing people, things and events.
Happenings	'What happened next?'

The debriefer asks how prepared people were for what happened, and concludes by bringing the debriefees into the present and asking them what thoughts and impressions are still around now.

Techniques

Coping with feelings
It is impossible for most people to tell their stories without expressing feelings, and some will be mentioned or will simply emerge. For example, when asked, 'What did you think when that happened?' the response may be to say, 'I felt that . . .', or to express a direct feeling, 'I was angry.' The debriefer must be aware of these overt, expressed feelings, but also of the hidden ones shown in body language or in the way words are spoken. These feelings should be noted, so that the debriefer can bring them into the Feelings Stage later. He acknowledges the feelings, but attempts to move to the thoughts that lie behind them:

Debriefer: What did you think when you saw the gun?
Debriefee: I was frightened.
Debriefer: When I asked what you thought when you saw the gun, you said you were frightened. Why were you

frightened?

Debriefee: [Pause.] I suppose it was because he could have shot me and I could be dead.

Debriefer: So, the thought behind that was 'I could have been killed'?

Debriefee: Yes, that's right. I thought he was going to shoot me, and now I could be dead and my family without a husband or father.

The debriefer asks why that particular feeling emerged, or uses the word 'because' in a questioning manner: 'You were frightened . . . because . . . ?' This technique should enable the debriefee to begin to see that although the feelings are present, the source lies in the incident rather than in himself.

Coping with information

The debriefer has to cope with a great deal of information, especially when dealing with a group, and sometimes he asks himself, 'Will I remember all this?' The basic techniques that are inherent in counselling and in listening skills* help him to remember:

- Prompting   Using observation of the debriefee's body language, and (minimal) verbal and non-verbal encouragement.
- Mirroring   Feeding back the information, using the same words as the debriefee.
- Paraphrasing   Using different words to say what the debriefee has said.
- Reflecting   Acknowledging the debriefee's feelings, emotions and reactions.

Using these techniques enables the debriefer to confirm that he is getting the story right, shows the debriefee that he is listening and understanding, and helps the debriefer to store the information and remember it.

---

* These skills are outlined in detail in *Listening and Helping in the Workplace*, Frank Parkinson, 1995.

Asking questions

Whether with a group or with an individual, the debriefer asks questions to elicit the facts of the story. The same questions are asked of everyone in turn; the technique is to ask the questions first in general, and then in particular. In the one-to-one Debriefing the debriefer does this by first saying which question he is going to ask, and then asking it.

Debriefer: Sylvia, I would like you to think back to before you were raped. It happened at ten o'clock at night. Go back to before then. I am going to ask you a number of questions about where you had been, who you were with, what you were thinking and doing and what happened. [He pauses.] First, where were you before it happened, and what were you doing?

This technique gives her time and space to consider her response, and helps to take her back to the situation before the rape took place; it moves the question from the general to the specific.

Similarly, in a group Debriefing the debriefer first presents the situation and then the question, or questions, to the whole group, while making firm eye contact with everyone. He then puts the question to the first person in the group.

Debriefer: I would like to ask you all what you were doing just before the incident took place, who you were with and what you were thinking and talking about. The accident happened at three o'clock, so I would like you all to think back to around five minutes or so before you were aware that anything was happening. [He pauses.] John, where were you and what were you doing at about five minutes to three?

He allows John to reply, mirrors or paraphrases, may ask another related question—and then moves on to the next person in the group.

The initial question depends on the nature of the incident. In an armed robbery that took place at eleven in the morning he will ask what they were all doing just before eleven. With police officers who have attended a road traffic accident he will ask what they were doing just before they heard about the accident on the radio or telephone. This will usually be after the incident has happened and it may take them some time to arrive at the scene. The object is to take them back into the normality of the situation that prevailed shortly before they were aware that anything was wrong.

Coping with the group

When everyone has responded to the initial question about what they were doing before they became involved in the incident, the debriefer asks each person to tell his or her own story. But rather than asking the first person to tell his story from beginning to end, which would take too long and bore or annoy the rest of the group, the technique is to ask questions that slowly take the story forward, each person filling in his or her part as appropriate. Like building a pyramid or doing a jigsaw, everyone puts in their individual pieces until the structure or picture is complete.

People will come into the story at different times. With an armed robbery in a bank, the debriefer asks each person what he or she was doing a few minutes before becoming aware of the robber or of the robbery taking place, and then asks everyone when they were first aware that something was wrong. This usually elicits different responses:

John: I was aware immediately the robber entered the branch.

Michael: I saw the robber only when the robbery was in progress.

Mary: I did not see the robber because I was making coffee in the rest-room.

Lucy: I saw the robber straight away.

Edith: I was sitting at a desk typing and was only aware when I heard the robber's angry voice.

Initially the story comes from John and Lucy, with the others being brought in when it reaches the point of their involvement. As he moves around the group, it is important that the debriefer keeps acknowledging those whose experiences come in at a later stage. John is first in the circle, then Michael, followed by Mary, Lucy and Edith. In this example, everyone has said what they were doing before the robbery and John has already told his story up to the entry of the robber. The debriefer is careful not to ignore Michael or Mary.

Debriefer: John, thank you for that. Michael, you have told us what you were thinking and doing before you were aware that the incident was taking place. I would like to go on and let the others tell us what was happening while you were looking at those files. Is that all right?

Michael: Yes. I would like to know. I've heard bits of the story, but not everything.

Debriefer: Mary, you said you didn't see the incident at all because you were in the back room making coffee and having a break and thinking about going to the cinema with your husband that evening. You came in when it was over. I would like to move on to Lucy because she saw the robber straight away, as did John. Is this all right?

Mary: Yes. I feel so stupid about not being there. I would like to know what happened and hear the details.

Debriefer: Lucy, you said you were dealing with Mrs Johnston and her five pounds, which she comes to pay in every Monday. What was it that made you think that something was wrong?

Lucy: I was finishing with Mrs Johnston and this man walked into the branch. Well, sort of hurried, I suppose, and I thought he looked a bit strange.

Debriefer: In what way did you think he looked strange?

The Debriefer allows Lucy to tell this part of the story as far as a brief description of the robber, and then moves on to Edith.

Debriefer: Edith, you didn't know anything was happening until you heard the robber's voice. I would like to

	ask John to tell some more of his story and then bring you in later when we hear about the robber's voice.
Edith:	Yes, that's all right. There was I, sitting minding my own business and it was all happening at the tills. I just wish I could have done something about it.
Debriefer:	That's a natural reaction and we'll look at it later. [Turns to John.] John, you, like Lucy, said you saw the robber. I would like you to freeze the picture and describe him. You can see him there. What did he look like and what was he wearing?

Coping with a lack of response

As already noted, not everyone will answer every question, and some may not speak at all.

> Before a group Debriefing, the senior manager had warned the debriefer that one woman did not want to be there. She had said that she would attend simply because she belonged to the team, but that she did not wish to answer any questions. He described her as 'the serious one in the team'. She was tall and slim and wore rather funereal clothes. She shook her head after every question, and did not speak a word. All the same, the debriefer stopped and briefly asked her each question, offering her an opportunity to reply. At the end of the Debriefing, when asked to make their final statements, she finally spoke: 'I didn't want to be here, but came because I belong to the team. I have found it helpful, and didn't think I would say as much as I have.' The debriefer believed that she had been debriefing herself as each question was asked and answering for herself internally, even though she had not spoken.

Because the debriefer puts the questions to the group first, the procedure encourages self-Debriefing. Even if they do not ultimately respond themselves, while others are replying all will usually be answering the questions internally.

These techniques are used in both the Facts and the Feelings Stages.

After the Introduction and asking people to give their names and roles, the debriefer moves on to the Facts Stage, and asks each person in turn what he or she was doing:

1 *Before* the incident.
2 *During* the incident.
3 *After* the incident.

1 BEFORE THE INCIDENT

The questions are based on the debriefer's knowledge of what happened and on the accumulating knowledge that he gathers from the replies of the debriefees. The debriefer needs to be able to think laterally, so that one question leads to other, related, questions:

> 'Where were you just before you heard about/became involved in the incident?'
> 'What was happening around you?'
> 'What was the weather like?' 'What were the road conditions/ traffic/crowds/interior of the room/car/aeroplane like?' 'Describe the hills/river/pavement/grass/trees/fields/etc.'
> 'Who were you with?' 'What was your relationship with them?'
> 'What were you doing/talking about/thinking about/listening to/discussing/looking at?' 'Was there anything in particular on your mind?'
> 'What were you planning to do later?'

Take, for example, another *armed robbery* that took place in an enclosed shopping centre where Sheila had gone to buy a jumper from Marks & Spencer for her mother's birthday. She was threatened by the robber and violently pushed to the ground.

Debriefer:	Sheila, why did you go into town on that particular day?
Sheila:	I went to buy a jumper for my mother.
Debriefer:	Was there any particular reason for buying her a

present?

Sheila: Yes, it's her birthday next week.

Debriefer: So you went to buy a jumper for her as a birthday gift. Did you have any particular jumper in mind?

Sheila: Yes. I had seen this nice blue one in M & S last time I was in the centre and thought she would like it.

Debriefer: You had something in mind to buy so decided to go into town on your own. What about the children? Did they go with you?

Sheila: They are both at the local school and I had to go and buy the jumper before I picked them up. I thought I had plenty of time.

Debriefer: So, you went to buy this particular blue jumper thinking that you had lots of time before collecting the children.

Sheila: Yes. I thought that if I could get it, it would save time later, as her birthday is next week and I have a lot to do in the next few days.

Debriefer: It sounds as though you were in a bit of a hurry.

Sheila: Yes, I suppose I was. I wanted to get back in time for the children, but I wasn't worried or anything and town isn't too far away.

Debriefer: Tell me how you got into town?

Sheila: I went in the car.

Debriefer: What was the weather like, and was it easy to get there?

Sheila: It was fine. There wasn't much traffic so it was easy and I parked in the multi-storey next to the shopping centre. There were plenty of free spaces.

Debriefer: So, it was a fine day and you drove into town, parked the car and walked into the centre. Was there a lift or stairs to the shopping level?

Sheila: Yes, there's a lift and stairs. I don't like lifts so I walked down the stairs.

Debriefer: Try to picture yourself walking down the stairs. Do you remember anything about it?

Sheila: Yes. There was a smell of urine, as usual.

Debriefer: And that's something you can remember now—the smell?

Sheila: Yes, it's horrible, so I walked as quickly as I could.

Debriefer: What did you notice when you first walked into the centre? Anything or anyone in particular?

Sheila: Well, it wasn't very busy, but I heard the music straight away.

Debriefer: Music?

Sheila: Yes. You know, that musak stuff?

Debriefer: So you heard the music immediately. Did you know where it was coming from and what kind of music it was?

Sheila: It was coming through the loud-speaker system. Jazzed-up classical music, but I didn't know what it was. It always irritates me.

Debriefer: Did you notice anything else?

Sheila: Yes. There were some young people shouting and laughing and I remember that cheered me up. I could also hear the water from the fountain and see a woman selling flowers. Then I saw this little old lady in front of me. It was strange really, because from the back she looked just like my mum.

Debriefer: You cheered up a bit, heard the water and then saw this little old lady. In what ways did she remind you of your mother?

Sheila: Well, she was about the same height and was walking with a stick like my mother does, with a slight limp.

Debriefer: Can you describe her for me? What she was wearing, for instance?

The debriefer will already have noticed the sensory impressions and feelings that he will need to remember for the next stages of the Debriefing:

Sensory impressions

- The blue jumper that Sheila had in mind.
- The smell of urine on the stairs—can she still recall it, or smell it now?
- The sound of the music, which irritated her.
- The sound of laughter, which cheered her up.
- The sound of the fountain.
- The sight of the little old lady reminding her of her mother.

Feelings

- Slight anxiety on her way there—she was in a hurry.
- Feeling disgusted by the smell on the stairs.
- Cheered up by the laughter—can she remember feeling this?
- Irritation at the music.
- How did she feel when she saw the little old lady?

Any of the sensory impressions can act as triggers for re-experiencing the incident. The next time Sheila walks down the stairs into the shopping centre the smell might make her feel panic or fear. The sound of the music and the laughter of other people might result in the return of the feelings associated with the incident. Next time she sees a blue jumper she might feel angry or frightened and not know why—these would be normal post-traumatic reactions. Part of the Debriefing process is therefore to pre-empt the possibility of these reactions occurring by creating awareness of them as well as exposure to the triggers. The debriefer is also attempting to take the debriefees back in time to the normal situation before the incident happened, then from that normality into the abnormality of the incident; and from there to the normality of reactions, then forward into the present.

A group Debriefing, as already mentioned, also includes those members of the team or group who were not present during the incident.

One team member who had been at home said that she was doing the ironing at the exact time of the incident, but was not informed about it until later that evening by telephone. Her main response, of guilt and anger at not being there to support her colleagues, came in the Feelings Stage.

The last question in this 'before' stage takes the participants to the point at which they were aware that something was happening or about to happen—for instance:

'When and why were you aware that something was wrong?'
'What made you think that something was about to happen?'
'How did you know that something was going to happen, or had happened?'
'When and how did you find out that the incident was taking place?'

These questions are based on the debriefer's knowledge of the incident. If two police officers had been in a patrol car when a message came through on the radio, the debriefer would ask them when the message came through, what the exact words were, what they had thought about it, what they did and how they got to the scene of the incident. With the woman in the shopping precinct, he would ask when she knew that something was wrong, then what she thought was happening, then what she saw.

2   THE FACTS: DURING THE INCIDENT

Each person is encouraged to talk through the incident, beginning with the moment when he or she was aware that something was wrong. This section continues to ask about thoughts, impressions, expectations and actions:

'How did you hear about/become involved in the incident?'
'Can you remember the words used?'
'What did you expect?'
'What happened?' 'How prepared were you for what happened?'
'What did you see?'

'What were your thoughts at the time?'
'What did you do, and why did you decide to do it?'

Continuing with the example of the woman in the shopping precinct:

Debriefer: So, you saw this old lady in front of you who reminded you of your mother and you have described her in detail. What happened next?

Sheila: Well, I saw this man running out of the shop carrying a bag and a gun. I couldn't believe it. He just pushed the old lady over and walked towards me.

Debriefer: Let's go back a little and look at how this happened. When were you first aware that something was wrong?

Sheila: Mmm . . . I heard a sort of shout. People's voices.

Debriefer: Can you remember what they were shouting or saying?

Sheila: No. It was just somebody shouting, like someone angry.

Debriefer: Somebody shouting. What kind of a shout was it? Loud, gruff, a scream?

Sheila: Just a high-pitched shout. I couldn't make out the words, but I knew that somebody was very upset or angry. It sounded like somebody shouting, 'Stop, stop!', but I can't be sure. I was told afterwards that it was the shop assistant.

Debriefer: What did you think when you heard this angry shouting?

Sheila: I don't know really. I was frightened. My mouth went all dry.

Debriefer: You were frightened, but what were you thinking and what made you frightened?

[The debriefer is moving her from feelings back to thoughts.]

Sheila: I don't exactly know. I just hate it when people are

angry and I thought, I hope they don't drag me in,
I'm in a hurry.

Debriefer: So, you thought that you might get involved in some
way in whatever was happening?

Sheila: Yes.

Debriefer: What happened next?

Sheila: I looked around and saw that the noise was coming
from the jeweller's shop over on my left and to the
front of me, just beside where the old lady was
walking.

Debriefer: What did you do and what happened?

Sheila: I stopped. Then I saw this man running out of the
shop and I sort of froze, like a statue, wondering
what it was about.

Debriefer: What did you think was happening, and what did
you expect?

Sheila: I don't know, really. It all happened so quickly. I
knew straight away that it was a robbery, but I
couldn't believe it—like it was happening to somebody else and not to me. I don't know what I
expected, but I thought immediately that there was
going to be trouble.

Debriefer: I would like you to slow down a bit if you can. We
are coming to the main part of the story. You heard
a shout, stood still and saw this man running out
of the shop. You knew immediately when you saw
him that it was a robbery. I know you have told the
police, but I would like you to describe him. It
might be painful, but I'd like you to do it again.

Sheila: I'll try. This always upsets me because I can still
see his face when I close my eyes. [Becomes upset.]

Debriefer: This is very difficult for you. Just try to push the
feelings away and imagine you are watching the
scene from a distance. If you can, tell me how he
ran out, how old he was and what he was wearing.

Sheila: [Pauses.] Well, he didn't run too quickly—more of
a fast walk. I don't know how old he was, but I

	would guess he was a few years younger than me. About eighteen, I think.
Debriefer:	How tall was he, and what was he wearing?
Sheila:	He was much taller than me, about the same as my husband—he's six feet. He had a yellow woollen hat on and a short, black denim jacket and a sort of green polo-neck shirt.
Debriefer:	Trousers and shoes?
Sheila:	Jeans, I think—dark blue. But it's his face and boots I remember.
Debriefer:	So, he was a tall young man dressed casually and you especially noticed his face and boots. Tell me what you noticed about his face?
Sheila:	It was his eyes. They looked so cold. As though nothing was happening. It frightened me because I expected him to be angry and in a hurry, but he wasn't. As cool as could be.
Debriefer:	Can you describe his eyes?
Sheila:	They were very dark and seemed to be staring at me—almost looking through me, as if to say, 'I'll get you if you try to stop me.' They were very frightening and I can see them now when I think about them.
Debriefer:	So, you thought that if you got in his way he might shoot you?
Sheila:	Yes, absolutely. That's what made me afraid. Especially with what he did to the old woman.
Debriefer:	You mean, when he pushed her to the floor?
Sheila:	Yes. He was so rough and just smashed her down with his hand—the one carrying the gun.
Debriefer:	What did you think—not feel—when he did this to her?
Sheila:	I felt, I mean, I thought, how can you do that to an old woman? What sort of a person does something like that?
Debriefer:	You thought that human beings don't behave like that?

Sheila: Yes, I did. It was awful. And I couldn't do anything
             to help her. I felt so useless.
Debriefer: You felt useless because . . . ?
Sheila: Because I couldn't do anything.
Debriefer: You were unable to help and, you said earlier, you
             were frozen to the spot.
Sheila: Yes. I just froze with shock.
Debriefer: Let's go back to his face because how he looked at
             you seems very important. Anything about the rest
             of his face that you remember?
Sheila: Yes. He had some teeth missing at the front, like
             he'd been playing rugby, in a fight or something,
             and he had a ring in his ear. A large one, more like
             a curtain ring.
Debriefer: So, his face was very significant and his eyes fright-
             ened you and he had some teeth missing. You also
             mentioned his boots. Tell me what you remember
             about them.
Sheila: Well, I didn't see them until I was on the floor.
Debriefer: Let's go back a bit again. Tell me what happened
             when he pushed the old woman to the floor. How
             did he do it and what did you see?

The debriefer now asks her to describe what happened to the old lady, then asks again what was strange or particular about the young man's boots. He also asks her to describe in detail the gun and the bag. This leads to questions about what happened next. In the incident, the man pushed the old lady to the floor, pointed the gun at the younger woman and told her to lie down. It was there that she saw his boots and thought that he was going to kick her. They were black Doc Martens. For a few seconds, they were just in front of her face as she lay on the floor; she could feel the cold, damp surface and smell antiseptic and stale cigarette ash. She is asked to say what happened next, what she was thinking, and then to talk through the story until the police came and the incident was over.

The debriefer should now be aware of further sensory impressions and feelings, although these are acknowledged rather than discussed:

Sensory impressions

- The sound of angry shouting.
- The sight of the robber's face, eyes and boots, and the gun.
- The sight of the old lady being pushed to the floor.
- The smell of the floor—antiseptic and stale cigarettes.
- The robber's voice—what accent? how angry? Can she remember it now?
- The cool, damp feel of the tiled floor.
- A mouth dry with fear and anxiety.

Feelings

- Shock and disbelief—'It can't be happening.'
- Anger that a man could behave in this way.
- Anxiety and concern about the way the old lady was treated.
- Fear at being threatened and about being shot or even killed, and that she might never see her family again.
- Helplessness at not being able to do anything.
- Helplessness concerning the old lady, who was only a few feet away.

These, with the previously noted reactions, will be stored away and brought up during the Feelings Stage, when sensory impressions, feelings and reactions are considered.

3 THE FACTS: AFTER THE INCIDENT

Here the debriefer moves on to look at what happened when the incident was over—he will need to judge when to end the story. In reality the story ends in the Debriefing when it considers the effects of the incidents on those involved. However, the actual incident should have an ending in the past, and the debriefer's decision as to exactly when this should be will depend on the nature of the incident and the involvement of the individual or group. Thus, another reason why the debriefer should know the facts about the incident beforehand is so that he can decide when to finish the story.

In the case of *an armed robbery* in a building society or other premises, it will be relevant to include in the story the time between the robber leaving and the staff returning to work the next day. This will include the arrival and subsequent departure of the police; the staff going home that evening and how people treated them, especially families and friends; what happened on the way to work next morning and when they arrived in the branch. This part of the story will probably be short, but the information will almost certainly be important. What they were thinking, how they were treated by others and how they coped towards the end of the incident—all lead from the incident to the after-effects, then to the Feelings Stage, then into the present. If a long time—perhaps some weeks—has elapsed since the incident, it will be relevant to ask what has happened and what people's reactions have been in the meantime, but still without looking at feelings.

With someone who has been *raped or injured*, the debriefer will probably end the story at the point when she went to hospital, or when she was examined by the doctor and gave her statement to the police, or when she went home that night; but looking at the interim period will again be important.

For police officers involved in an incident the story will probably end at the point when they returned to their car or to the station, or went off duty and then home; for fire and rescue officers it will end when they returned to the watch-room or went off duty. Questions such as these may be asked:

'What happened when the police came and after they left?'
'How did they and others treat you?'
'What happened when you went home, and how did your family and friends react?'
'What happened when you went to work the next day?'

Continuing with the incident involving the woman who went

to buy a jumper, the robber has gone and she is lying on the floor:

Debriefer: So, the robber knocked you to the floor, you saw his boots and thought that he would kick you, and then he was gone. But you didn't see him go—it was only that you couldn't see his boots any more. You were aware of the old lady lying in front of you, groaning. What happened next?

Sheila: I just lay there, terrified and frozen rigid. I daren't move in case he was still there. I just couldn't do anything. I daredn't do anything. Then, this voice told me to get up and that it was all right, he had gone. A man was leaning over me and helped me up. The next thing I remember is sitting down in a café with a young police officer asking me if I was all right, and then the ambulance came. I remember the sound of the sirens.

The debriefer now asks for details about:

- The man who helped her up—what he said and did.
- Whether anyone else helped, and what she thought of those who were standing around watching.
- How she got into the café.
- The police officer and his involvement.
- The ambulance arriving, and going to hospital for a check-up.
- The old woman—what happened to her and whether there was any contact with her after the incident.

She might have thoughts and reactions about the way others had behaved towards her: witnesses, the police and hospital staff. She would also be concerned about the old woman; questions might arise, such as 'Why didn't anyone do anything to help?' Those involved after the incident might have done or said something unhelpful, even unintentionally, and led to feelings of anger, resentment or bitterness in Sheila.

After her medical check-up she returned home, by which time

her husband was there and the children had been collected from school by a neighbour.

Debriefer: You were taken home in a taxi, having been told that you were all right physically and after making a statement to the police. You said that the hospital staff and the police were very sympathetic. What were you thinking on your way home in the taxi?

Sheila: I was feeling much better and getting over the initial shock, but I was still worried about the old lady. She had been kept in hospital, but at that time I didn't know how she was. They had got me a taxi and said that I should contact my GP the next day. I was a bit worried about how my husband would react, but my neighbour had told me on the phone that he and the children were fine.

Debriefer: What were you thinking about how your husband might react?

Sheila: Well, he's not one for worrying. I thought he would be all right with me, but that he would tell me not to get upset. He thinks that you have to get on with life and put things behind you. I suppose he finds it difficult to show his feelings.

Debriefer: You thought he would be supportive, but that he wouldn't understand how you felt?

Sheila: Yes, I hoped he would help, but he doesn't like it when I get upset.

Debriefer: So what happened? How *did* he and the children react? Talk it through from when the taxi arrived home.

It will be important to consider how supportive her husband was and how she reacted to his response. The debriefer will be concerned that she should have someone understanding to talk to—this will be raised in the third, Future, stage.

The sensory impressions and feelings that the Debriefer might note are:

Sensory impressions

- The silence when Sheila walked into the house.
- The sight of the concerned faces of her children.
- The unconcerned sound of her husband's voice.
- The need for a hug, which she got from the children, but not from her husband.

Feelings

- Anger at what she saw as the lack of concern of bystanders. She thought they should have done more to help.
- Fear of the robber's boots and of being kicked.
- Guilt and concern about the old lady.
- Concern, and some anger, about the lack of response and support from her husband.
- Tension in trying to keep her feelings under control at home because she didn't want to upset her husband.
- A feeling of hopelessness and failure at not being able to do anything about the robber or to help the old lady.

At the end of this Facts Stage the debriefer should possess a detailed knowledge of what happened and how the various people were involved, what they did and how they reacted, as well as some information about feelings and emotional reactions.

In the case of Sheila, he already has a list of sensory impressions and feelings stored away which will be raised during the next stage (see Chapter 11). By the end of the Facts Stage these could be:

Sensory impressions

- Smells: urine on the stairs.
                disinfectant and cigarette ash on the tiled floor.
- Sounds: music which irritated her.
                laughter which cheered her up.
                the noise of the fountain.
                angry shouting.

the robber's voice.

the sound of the police and ambulance sirens.

silence when she went home.

her husband's unconcerned voice.

- Sights: the old lady reminding her of her mother.

the blue jumper.

the robber's face, eyes and boots, and the gun.

the old lady being pushed to the floor.

the concerned faces of her children.

- Touch: the floor—tiled.

the need for a hug—which she got from her children, but not from her husband.

- Taste: a dry mouth.

Feelings

- Anxiety: because she was in a hurry.

about the way the old lady was treated.

- Disgust: the smell on the stairs made her feel horrible.
- Happiness: the laughter of others cheered her up.
- Shock: feeling frozen like a statue.
- Disbelief: 'It can't be happening.'
- Guilt: at her inability to help the old lady.
- Anger: at the robber for what he did.

at the perceived lack of concern of the bystanders.

at her husband's lack of concern and support.

at having to control her feelings at home.

at herself for not having done something to help.

- Fear: at being threatened and about the possibility of being shot or killed.

that she might never see her family again.

when the old lady was pushed down.

of the boots and of being kicked.

- Helplessness: at not being able to do anything.
  at not being able to go to the aid of the old lady, who was only a few feet away.
- Failure: at not having been able to help the old lady.

Some of these feelings may not be important, but since the debriefer cannot yet judge which are and which are not, they should all be mentioned in the next stage of the Debriefing.

Ending the Facts Stage
The debriefer will not have kept himself aloof and remote from the story during this stage, but will have acknowledged feelings and reactions as and when they emerged, before moving the debriefee gently back to the facts that lie behind the feelings. He will not move straight on to the Feelings Stage without making a transitional statement, which will include a brief summing-up and an explanation of what is to happen next. With Sheila it might go like this:

Debriefer: Thank you for telling me the story. It was a frightening experience for you and you have included a great deal of information. There have been some feelings bubbling below the surface such as shock and disbelief, fear and anger, helplessness and a sense of failure at not being able to do anything. Before I move on to the next stage, I would like to ask you one final question. What are you left with now as you sit here in the Debriefing? What thoughts are uppermost in your mind?

Sheila: I still can't believe it happened. It's like a bad dream, as though it happened to someone else. Everything seems to be churning around inside me.

Debriefer: I would like to move on to the next stage in the Debriefing, the Feelings Stage, and look at the emotions and reactions. In order to do this, I first want to ask about the sensory impressions—the sights, sounds and smells and so on that you associate with the incident—and then look at specific feelings and reactions.

So he begins by looking at the sensory impressions, and this leads directly on to the Feelings Stage.

11   Stage 2: The Feelings

Moving from facts to feelings and emotions is not a sudden change, because both the debriefer and the debriefees will be aware that some emotional and physical reactions have already emerged during the telling of the story. However, as already noted, the debriefer does not focus immediately on these, but uses sensory impressions as the means of making the transition. Moreover, experiencing sensory impressions in the future may resurrect the feelings from the incident that are associated with them: a smell, a sight, a sound, a taste or a touch can act as a trigger for reactions. These reactions are likely to be more difficult to handle if the debriefees are unable to make the connection between the present experience and the past event. As well as helping them to do this, the Debriefing should reduce the level of reactions. The debriefees should be enabled by their grasp of the facts that have been established in Stage 1 to recognise these reactions, understand what their role is in the present, and be able to identify their source in the traumatic incident.

FROM FACTS TO REACTIONS

The information the debriefer has at the beginning of this stage is based on the stories told by each debriefee, and some of these, as we have seen, will have included sensory impressions experienced at the time. Debriefees may also experience sensory reactions later, but be unaware of where they come from. In a car crash, for instance, the touch of the steering-wheel, the sound of screeching tyres or an ambulance siren, a dry mouth, the sight of the other car, the antiseptic smell of the hospital—all are implicit in the story and can trigger reactions associated with them. The debriefer's task is to use the information given in their stories to help the debriefees to identify and understand their emotional and physical reactions, and to bring out reactions that have not yet been mentioned.

Take, for instance, the senses of sight and touch.

Sight

The debriefer asks the debriefees to concentrate on sights or images deriving from the story which may have caused or led to reactions:

Debriefer: You said that you could see the man's face through the windscreen of the car as it hurtled towards you. Is there anything you can recall about it, or that you especially noticed?

Debriefee: Well, I did see his face, but it all happened so quickly that I can't remember anything about it.

Debriefer: Close your eyes, freeze the picture and concentrate on his face. What can you see?

Debriefee: [Long pause.] I can see the face and ... and I can see he's shouting something.

Debriefer: Keep looking at him. Do you see anything about his face?

Debriefee: I can still see his face ... he was wearing dark glasses. I'd forgotten that. Big ones with large yellow frames. Then his hands come up and I just feel the shock of knowing he is going to crash into me.

The debriefer has identified a particular sight, the dark glasses, apparently forgotten by the debriefee. Seeing dark glasses with yellow frames at some time in the future might trigger disturbing emotional or physical reactions—anything from a mounting sense of unease to fear, panic and helplessness, shaking and sweating. Revealing the forgotten image does not prevent, but can prepare the debriefee for and pre-empt, any possible future reactions.

Touch

The debriefee in the car accident has talked about the crash, but has not mentioned the steering-wheel.

Debriefer: You haven't talked about the steering-wheel. Can you remember holding it?

Debriefee: Yes. I was clutching it tightly just before the accident—hanging on like grim death.

Debriefer: Has this bothered you in any way since?

Debriefee: Well, I can remember it, but it doesn't bother me. Except that when I got into my partner's car to drive it the other day I had a strange feeling come over me.

Debriefer: What was that?

Debriefee: It was like holding something burning, and I started to feel frightened and to panic. I sat there shaking for a few moments, and then I was all right.

Debriefer: Why did you react like that, feeling fear and panicking?

Debriefee: I suppose holding it reminded me of the accident.

The debriefer has identified the fact that holding a steering-wheel has triggered reactions of fear and panic and might do the same in the future.

Differences in facts

Although stories will be fairly consistent, there may be minor differences which do not usually matter and so do not need to be resolved. But where the differences seem to be important they should be acknowledged, because of the reactions they might cause later.

In a Debriefing after a robbery, three people said that the criminal was wearing a hat, but disagreed as to what kind it was. One said it was a red woollen hat, another that it was a red baseball cap and the third that it was a black baseball cap. Each of these differences could lead to a reaction: the sight of a baseball cap, red or black, might cause two of the participants to feel anxiety or fear; a red woollen hat might cause similar reactions in the third. In this case, the problem was resolved later by the pictures from the security camera, which showed that he was wearing a red baseball cap.

The debriefer's skill entails absorbing the information and then applying lateral thinking: what additional information is implied in the story, and what feelings and sensory reactions might result from a particular fact or piece of information?

REACTIONS

Reactions to traumatic incidents can be of two kinds: overt and expressed, or covert, and these will vary according to the debriefees and the nature of the incident.

Overt reactions

- What reactions have been mentioned, or have emerged in telling the story?

The debriefer will already have seen and heard specific emotional and physical reactions during the Facts Stage. For example, in the story involving the robbery in the shopping precinct Sheila expressed anxiety, fear, disbelief, hopelessness, helplessness and anger. These overt feelings and reactions, and any sensory impressions associated with them, are brought out by the debriefer and related to their place in the story.

Covert reactions

- What reactions have not been mentioned, but are common to this kind of incident?
- What emotions and reactions were hinted at, either in body language or in the way the words were expressed or the story was told?

These are reactions that the debriefer might expect from Sheila or from anyone else involved in such an incident, but that have not been expressed. Some might have been mentioned or even trivialised by the debriefee, or shown in her body language or in the way she speaks.

Debriefer: Sheila, when you talked about the other shoppers who were standing around you said, 'They just stood there', and you emphasised the words. What did you mean by this?

Sheila: They didn't do anything, did they? Standing there like lemons, just watching. It was ages before they came to help. I suppose I am angry about it now, even though I know they would have been as frightened as I was. It's anger—anger because they were safe, I suppose, and I wasn't. I saw a group of people standing talking the other day and I wanted to go over to them and say, 'What would you lot do if you saw a robbery taking place? Nothing.' It made me feel angry again just seeing them.

Debriefer: You have identified that you were angry with them and have re-experienced it since then with another group of people, so groups of people might make you feel angry. But you did also say later that some of them were helpful.

Sheila: Yes, they were. I suppose the anger is just shock and the fact that I felt so helpless. When it was over, they were concerned about me and the old lady and one of them took me into the café and bought me a coffee, but I still feel angry.

The debriefer has helped Sheila to identify her anger at other shoppers, the fact that a group of people might trigger this feeling again, and that this is probably due to her feeling of helplessness.

Differences in reactions

The most common reactions in any traumatic incident, as we have seen, are shock, disbelief, fear, anger and helplessness. These are natural and expected, but there are many other possible reactions, some of which are positive, and they vary with different incidents and with different individuals and groups.

Some will blame themselves; others will look for someone or something else to blame. Some will experience pointlessness, detachment and isolation, a sense of unreality, emptiness or inner conflict; others will feel totally involved and believe that they have done their best. Some will ask questions about meaning and purpose and feel picked on; some will feel hopeless and utterly helpless; others will have a sense of achievement, confidence and hope. Some will cope immediately, or in the short term; others will develop adverse physical or psychological reactions which deepen as time passes.

Because of this great variety of possible reactions, before the Debriefing the debriefer should prepare a check-list of possible reactions, bearing in mind (1) the kinds of people involved, and (2) the nature of the incident.

1 The kinds of people involved

There can be differences between the ways that professionals and non-professionals react. Because of their training and experience and the support they receive, professionals usually cope by controlling and suppressing their emotions. A group of police or fire and rescue officers, for instance, may be more resistant to the Debriefing process than are customers present at an armed robbery or passengers involved in a hostage situation. Deeply religious people may initially feel calm and accepting and experience an increased sense of purpose, but later become confused and angry and question the existence of God. Where there have been deaths, medical personnel may have strong feelings of failure, even if they believe that they have done their best. After combat experience soldiers may be elated and confident, but later question their behaviour and actions, and move from elation at being alive to self-justification, then anger, survivor guilt and remorse.

2 The nature of the incident

After a rape, the victim is likely to have strong feelings of disbelief and fear, and of being soiled and used; she may also experience helplessness, a numbing of feelings, physical reactions of pain and distress and a desire to wash frequently. Being raped can lead to a lack of trust in men, low self-esteem, a change in personal image, isolation and sexual problems. After a car crash feelings of disbelief and anger are probable, as well as fear of getting into a car again. After a mugging, there are likely to be reactions of shock, anger and disbelief, but also of having been victimised. A major disaster can result in feelings of fear and helplessness, and of life and the world being out of control. Reactions to events that are sudden and devastating may be different from those where the stress is intermittent or on-going, and reactions to long periods of stress may be stronger and more difficult to cope with. This is discussed in Chapter 2 under Type 1 and Type 2 traumatic events (pages 35–6), and the use of Debriefing in such situations is dealt with in Chapter 14.

Difficulties with reactions

If, as sometimes happens, debriefees find it difficult to get in touch with their sensory impressions, one method of enabling them to do so is to ask them to think of a particular sense and try to imagine it in the present (see Check-list 2):

Smell

Debriefer: You said that you could smell petrol after the crash. Can you smell it now?
John: I don't think so.
Debriefer: I would like you to close your eyes and slowly sniff and see if you can experience the smell.
John: [Closes his eyes and sniffs.] Yes, I can smell it, but it doesn't really disturb me. I can live with it.
Debriefer: It doesn't affect you, but you can still smell it. Mary, what about the smell of petrol for you?
Mary: Oh, yes. I can smell it now. In fact, when I filled the car up the other day, the smell of petrol took me right back to the crash and I felt frightened. I could almost feel the accident happening again.

Check-list 2: Sensory impressions

Sounds?	'What sounds can you remember from the incident?' 'The wind or the rain?' 'Birds or animals?' 'Police or ambulance sirens?' 'Screeching metal or tyres, sounds of a crash, an explosion?' 'What human sounds did you hear?—shouting, screaming, moaning?' 'What were the exact words?' 'Was there a significant silence at any stage?'
Smells?	'What can you remember smelling?' 'After-shave, sweat, breath, alcohol, blood, petrol, oil, burning wood, food, smoke?'
Touch?	'What can you remember touching?' 'Wood, metal, water?' 'Did anyone or anything touch you?' 'How?'
Taste?	'What did you taste?' 'Water, oil, petrol, blood, medicine, burning?' 'Was your mouth dry?'
Sights?	'What images come into your mind from the incident?'

What are the debriefees' memories and feelings about these now?
Ask about all the senses, even if they are not mentioned.
What reactions have they had to sensory impressions since the incident?
'What reactions do you still have *now*?'

Sight

Debriefer: You mentioned the man's eyes and that they were horrible, cold and threatening. Can you see them now?

Judith: No, not really.

Debriefer: Close your eyes and think of those eyes. Can you see them, and how do they make you feel?

Judith: I can now. They look like black points of light

staring at me and threatening to get me.

This approach should be used only with those senses which seem to be significant or disturbing, or where debriefees find it difficult to make contact with the feelings that they might generate. Used too frequently, it becomes repetitive, clinical and boring.

SENSORY IMPRESSIONS: SIGHTS, SOUNDS, SMELLS, TOUCH, TASTE

The debriefer begins by going back to the story and asking about specific sensory reactions. He may choose to ask about those that appear to be the least disturbing, but some debriefers prefer to begin with the most disturbing, believing that tackling these will enable the debriefees to move into feelings more easily.

Because some people may be unaware of what sensory impressions they have experienced, the basic method is to take *all five senses* and ask about each one in turn. There are two main ways in which this can be done: (1) the specific method and (2) the general method. The specific method gradually works through the story, asking about certain incidents and about particular reactions to them. The general method, as its name implies, asks the debriefees for a much more general response, usually takes less time, and is more useful for a large group.

1 The specific method

The debriefer looks at sensory impressions, both overt and covert, in chronological order as associated with particular experiences in the incident.

For example, in the story involving Sheila, the debriefer remembers that certain *sounds* have been mentioned by her: people laughing; angry voices and the robber's voice; the wail of police and ambulance sirens. He is also aware that Sheila did not mention anything about sounds when the robber walked away.

Overt reaction

- *Laughter*

Debriefer: I would like you to concentrate on the sounds you associate with the incident. At the beginning of the story, you mentioned the sound of people laughing and you said that this made you feel good. Are you able to hear that sound again, and how does it make you feel?

Sheila: Yes. I remember it did make me feel happy and I smiled at the time. It still makes me feel good, although I didn't know what was going to happen.

- *Angry shouting*

Debriefer: You mentioned the sound of angry shouting and of someone who was obviously upset. Can you recall this sound?

Sheila: Yes, it was confusing at the time, and frightening because I knew something was wrong but didn't know what it was except that someone was angry.

Debriefer: What kind of a shout was it? Can you remember the exact words?

- *The robber's voice*

Debriefer: The sound of the robber's voice seemed to be important to you: angry, threatening and intimidating. You talked about his exact words and how he said them. Are you able to recall that sound now?

Sheila: I can still hear his voice. I hear it when I go to bed at night and it sometimes comes into my mind during the day when I'm doing nothing. It's very frightening.

Debriefer: What is he saying and how does it make you feel?

● *Police and ambulance sirens*

Debriefer: When the incident was over, you said that you could
              hear the police and ambulance sirens. How powerful
              are those sounds now as you sit here?

Sheila: I remember them, but they don't upset me. I heard
              a police siren yesterday when I was out walking
              the dog and it didn't worry me. I just thought, I
              wonder if it's another robbery.

Covert reactions

● *Sounds*

Debriefer: You said you heard the sound of police and ambu-
              lance sirens. Do you remember hearing anything
              between the robber leaving and these sounds?

Sheila: Well, I can remember there was a horrible silence.
              It seemed to last a thousand years and I felt that
              nobody would help me. I felt so frightened and
              alone and was shaking with cold. Then there was
              a gabble of voices and I remember this man telling
              me that it was all right and I could get up. I was
              relieved, but also angry that nobody had helped us
              earlier. What were they all doing? Just standing
              there watching?

Debriefer: You remember the ominous silence, the voice of a
              man asking you to get up and you felt angry. How
              do you feel about this now?

If the debriefee recalls any sounds so far not mentioned, the
debriefer asks her to imagine them again and to be aware of what
reactions they cause now.

The other senses are looked at in the same way. If a sense has
not been mentioned, the debriefer still includes it.

● *Touch*

Debriefer: I realise that you haven't mentioned the sense of

	touch, but you touched, and were touched by, a number of things in the incident. You said you were thrown to the floor by the robber. Can you recall when he grabbed you?
Sheila:	Yes, I can. He grabbed hold of me and threw me to the floor. I've still got the marks on my arm.
Debriefer:	This violence is something you remember, and you have the bruises to show it and to remind you?
Sheila:	Yes. My husband touched my arm last night and I pulled away. I know it sounds silly, but it reminded me of the robber because he grabbed me in the same place.
Debriefer:	You said that the robber grabbed your arm and threw you to the floor and you can still recall this, especially when the bruises remind you or someone touches you there. Show me exactly how he grabbed you.
	[Sheila does so.]
Debriefer:	What about the feel of the floor? He threw you down and you were lying there. What was that like?
Sheila:	It was cold and hard and felt as though it was a wall I wanted to go through to get away, but couldn't. I could also smell disinfectant and cigarette ends . . .

After each response, the debriefer asks further questions in order to explore the strength of the feeling connected with the sensory impression concerned, to see how powerfully it is around now, and whether or not it is likely to trigger re-experiencing in the future. This procedure gives debriefees permission to express emotions and enables the feelings associated with sensory impressions to come to the surface.

Experiences after the incident
When all the sensory impressions have been explored, the debriefer asks which of them have been experienced between the end of the incident and the Debriefing.

Debriefer:	Sheila, I want to ask you about any reactions you have had in the last few days since the robbery. Have you experienced any reactions recently?
Sheila:	Well, I don't know if it's important, but I don't like my children to play with toy guns any more. Thomas had one the other day and was waving it about. I asked him to stop and said that I didn't like guns, so he went outside to play. I don't want to scare them, like I was scared, but it just made me feel a bit peculiar. I suppose I'll get used to it.
Debriefer:	The sight of a gun, even a plastic toy, made you feel strange because it reminded you of the robbery and how frightened you were. You feel that you don't want to upset the children unnecessarily, but you do know why you felt like that?
Sheila:	Yes, I do and I think I can cope with it.
Debriefer:	All right. Any other sensations since then?

The debriefer asks Sheila to look at any other sensory reactions: the sounds and smells, the sensations of touch and taste.

Experiences now
This section ends with the debriefer encouraging Sheila to look at what sensory impressions are still around in the Debriefing.

Debriefer:	Are there any of these around now, as you sit here?
Sheila:	Yes. I suppose the most frightening is the sight of the gun and his boots—and his eyes. I can see them all now if I close my eyes.
Debriefer:	Can you close your eyes now, and tell me what you see?
Sheila:	It's the gun. I can see it pointing at me as he waves it around and threatens me.
Debriefer:	And that's something that frightens you?
Sheila:	Yes. But it's also his face and eyes.
Debriefer:	Tell me some more about this image . . .

The debriefer can also pre-empt other possible future experiences, such as identity parades and court appearances.

Debriefer: How would you feel if you had to look at photographs or attend an identification parade and saw the man again?

Sheila: I don't know. The police want me to look at some photographs later today, but my sister is going with me, so I should be all right.

Debriefer: And you find that she understands and can help?

Sheila: Yes. We've always been close and she knows how I feel. I'll be all right with her, even if I do get upset.

Here the debriefer is beginning to encourage her to think about support, which will come in Stage 3. When all the senses have been explored, he moves on to look at specific feelings, emotions and reactions.

2 The general method

The debriefer asks about sensory impressions by taking each sense in turn and asking what the debriefees remember generally, in relation to that sense, from the whole incident. The technique is to take one sense, give time for thought, and then ask about it.

Here the debriefer addresses everyone in the group after an armed robbery in a bank:

Debriefer: I would like you to concentrate on sensory impressions: on the sights, sounds and smells, and the touch and taste sensations that you associate with the incident. Smell seems to have been important, so let's look at it now. Can you think of anything you remember smelling at any time during the incident? [He pauses.] Paul, what smell or smells do you associate with the robbery when you think about it?

Paul: Well, I think the main thing I could smell was the

breath of the robber when he leaned across and told me to give him the money. It was horrible.

Debriefer: The smell of bad breath. Anything in particular?

Paul: Well, it was not just bad breath, but alcohol. Whisky, I think. He had obviously geared himself up for the robbery. Dutch courage, I suppose.

Debriefer: So it was bad breath and whisky. Any other smell?

Paul: Not really. Oh, yes! I remember the strong smell of perfume when Rachel hugged me when it was all over. It was lovely and made me feel better— you know, that someone cared?

Debriefer: A comforting hug and the smell of perfume. Rachel, what perfume was it?

Rachel: It was 'Morning Mist'. I've worn it for years.

Debriefer: What does this smell do for you, Paul? Rachel still wears it.

Paul: I can smell it whenever she is around. I think of the robbery, but it makes me feel good. Safe, I suppose.

Debriefer: So that particular smell is positive for you, and even if it reminds you of the incident it makes you feel good. Any smells later?

Paul: No. None that I can think of.

Debriefer: What about when you went home?

Paul: Just the warm smell of the house as I walked through the door and the smell of my children when I hugged them. It was so good that I just burst into tears.

Debriefer: And you can recall that warm, safe feeling now?

Paul: Oh, yes! I was glad to be alive after what happened.

Debriefer: So you could smell bad breath, but also the good, strong smells of perfume and then your home, which helped and comforted you. Are any of these still around for you?

Paul: Not really, except that I feel thankful for my home and family when I walk into my house. I also like the smell of Rachel's perfume. It's a sort of

	reminder of the robbery, but also of how we coped.
Debriefer:	Part of the way you coped was the support you gave each other and being grateful for your life and family.
Paul:	Yes.
Debriefer:	Paul, thank you for that. Diana, what about you and smells from the incident? Throughout the whole incident, what can you recall?
Diana:	No particular smells, except that I was making coffee in the rest-room when the robbery happened and I didn't see or hear anything until it was all over. Every time I do that now, and smell the coffee, I remember the robbery taking place and wonder if it's happening again. I know it sounds stupid, but I sometimes feel so helpless and useless.
Debriefer:	The coffee smell brings back memories of the robbery, and you feel that you should have been there with the others.
Diana:	Yes. I know it wouldn't have made any difference, but they were suffering and I was OK. It was all right for me, safe and sound, singing away to myself, but they could be dead now.
Debriefer:	And that makes you feel bad?
Diana:	Yes. I still feel guilty for not being there.
Paul:	I'd like to say something, if I may. I'm glad Diana wasn't with us, even if it does make her feel guilty. She shouldn't feel like that. It's not her fault that she wasn't there, and anyway it was the robber who started this whole thing.
Debriefer:	Diana, you've heard what Paul has said. What do you feel about that?

Comments from others, such as the interventions of Rachel and Paul, can be helpful and supportive and, although they break up the progression around the circle, should be allowed and sometimes encouraged. The debriefer can ask a debriefee how she feels about what someone else has said, or even ask the group.

Debriefer: Diana has said that she feels awful about not being with you when the robbery took place. She was safe in the back making coffee and singing. Have you any comments about that?

[This question could be put to Paul or Rachel, or asked generally.]

Rachel: Yes. I think I can understand how she feels, but it's not her fault. She said she was going to make some coffee and I said I'd join her in a few minutes. When it was all over and she came in she just sat with me for a while with her arm around me, then I just talked and talked while she held my hand.

Debriefer: Paul?

Paul: I'd agree with that. Anyway, she's always singing. It cheers us up. She might feel guilty—and that *is* how she feels—but she could not have done anything. I know I was grateful for the way she behaved afterwards. She sort of gave us strength, telephoning the police and making coffee and tea and keeping the system going. We were so shocked that it was good to see that somebody was coping.

Debriefer: You both feel very firmly that it's not Diana's fault that she wasn't there, even if she does feel guilty—and she's entitled to feel that. You both also say that she was a great support to you afterwards.

Paul/Rachel: Yes.

Debriefer: Diana, how do you feel about what Paul and Rachel have said?

Diana: It makes me feel better, but I still feel a bit guilty. I just wanted to be there to help.

Rachel: But you did help by looking after us when it was over and by almost taking charge. You kept us together.

Such comments as these are usually helpful, but the debriefer should not allow this to become a general discussion about guilt or about what might have happened had Diana been there, or if she had come in half-way through the robbery. The points have been made by Rachel and Paul, and should be left to stand. The debriefer briefly sums up what has been said and then moves on.

When smells have been dealt with, the debriefer then asks about sights, touch, tastes and sounds in the same way.

Experiences after the incident

As with the specific method, the debriefer asks which, if any, of these sensory impressions have been experienced between the time of the incident and the Debriefing. Diana has already said that the smell of coffee has reminded her of the incident and of the fact that she was not there with the others. It is important to find out if there has been any re-experiencing or other reactions that can be attributed to sensory impressions remaining from the incident.

Debriefer: It is three days since the incident and you have mentioned a number of sensory impressions that you experienced during and immediately after the robbery. Between the end of the incident, when you all returned to work the next day, and today, have there been any significant reactions? Anything that has triggered reactions? Any images coming into your minds, or any smells or sounds? Diana, you mentioned the smell of coffee reminding you of the robbery. Has that persisted, and is it disturbing?

Diana: No, not really, but when I make the coffee I remember what I was doing when the robbery took place.

Debriefer: Has this happened when you make coffee at home?

Diana: No, just at work, and not every time I make it.

Debriefer: OK. So you are aware of what the smell of coffee can do? where the reaction comes from?

Diana: Yes, but that's all right.

Debriefer: Paul, anything for you?

Paul: Not that I can think of, except that I jumped a bit the other day when a man about the same age as the robber and wearing similar clothes rushed into

	the branch, the door banged behind him, and for one second I thought, 'It's happening again.' It was just for a second, and then I knew I was all right.
Debriefer:	Something like that can happen and trigger a natural reaction. Anything else?
Paul:	Not really, except that I do occasionally get a bit up-tight when I'm on my way to work and wonder what sort of a day it will be.
Debriefer:	What do you mean, up-tight?
Paul:	Well, a bit anxious, I suppose. I keep looking around almost as though I expect the robber to be there watching me. I know they haven't caught him yet, and I think I'll feel better when they do.

Experiences now

The debriefer looks at what reactions are present now.

This examination of what has happened since the incident should lead on to looking at specific feelings and emotions.

FEELINGS, EMOTIONS AND PHYSICAL REACTIONS

The debriefer already has a list of emotions and reactions that have emerged during the telling of the story, and may be aware that other feelings and reactions are also present. These reactions are not just emotional—they can also be physical (see Check-list 3). The debriefer will need to note any distressing reactions that might not be directly connected with the incident. He considers what feelings, emotions and reactions are:

- *Overt*—have emerged in telling the story, or have been sensed through body language or verbal expression.
- *Covert*—might have been experienced, but have not been mentioned.

As with sensory impressions, he can choose between two methods of working: (1) the specific and (2) the general.

Check-list 3: Feelings, emotions and physical reactions

Feelings   Look for *overt* and *covert* feelings.
FEAR. HELPLESSNESS. FRUSTRATION. ANGER. RAGE. GUILT.
SADNESS. DEPRESSION. SENSE OF ISOLATION. REGRET.
BITTERNESS. ANXIETY. UNPREPAREDNESS. SENSE OF UNREALITY.
SENSE OF ABNORMALITY. SENSE OF LOSS. EMPTINESS. CONFLICT.
SENSE OF POINTLESSNESS. SENSE OF BEING A PAWN IN A GAME.
DETACHMENT. SENSE OF TIME SLOWING DOWN. SENSE OF
REJECTION.

'Why me/him/her/us?'
'When did you cry or feel upset?'
'When did you feel annoyed or angry? swear, shout or scream?'
'Why did you feel or do these things?'
'What did you feel about those around you (in the team or
group)?'
'What did you feel about the criminal and about the police?'
'What did you feel about your family's and colleagues'
reactions?' 'In what ways were they unhelpful or helpful?'

Physical reactions
PALPITATIONS. SWEATING. FAINTING BOUTS. STOMACH PAINS.
CHEST PAINS. SLEEPLESSNESS. DIFFICULTY IN FALLING ASLEEP
OR STAYING AWAKE. SHAKING.

'What was the worst thing for you about the incident?'
'What reactions have you experienced since the incident?'
'What do you feel *now* as you sit here?'

---

1 The specific method
The specific method works chronologically through the incident,
asking about feelings and emotional and other reactions:

Before the incident.
During the incident.
After the incident.
Between the incident and the Debriefing.

Now, in the Debriefing.

The debriefer starts at the beginning of the story, focusing on specific parts of the incident.

Debriefer: Sheila, we have looked at sensory impressions, and you have had many reactions to what you experienced. We now move on to look at feelings and emotions. You said you went into town to buy a jumper for your mother. What were you feeling about this on your way into town?

Sheila: I was pleased, really. I was in a bit of a hurry and a bit anxious, but I also felt good because I knew what I wanted to buy and wasn't going to be looking around the shops for ages. I was happy, but in a rush.

Debriefer: So you felt good, but a little anxious. What about when you parked the car and walked down the stairs?

Sheila: I still felt good, but the horrible smell on the stairs upset me and I thought of the pathetic people who had done it. Still, when I walked into the shopping centre I heard the people laughing and this cheered me up again.

Debriefer: You went from feeling good, to feeling disgusted at the smell on the stairs, and then back to feeling happy. What about the music?

Sheila: That just made me feel angry—it always does— but I just switch my mind off it.

Debriefer: So there was a change in mood from happy to uncomfortable, and then happy and a bit angry, although you put the music out of your mind. How did you feel when you saw the old lady?

Sheila: I got a bit of a start, really, because she looked like my mother, as I have said, but I knew it couldn't be her. Mind you, I felt a bit sorry for her because she looked so alone, hobbling along on her own. I felt like going up to her and asking her if she would like to have coffee with me. My dad died two years ago, so I suppose that made me feel that way. It made me feel a bit sad. I felt even worse when she was pushed over.

Debriefer: You experienced a mixture of feelings: happy and then surprised at seeing the old lady, and then sorry and sad because this reminded you of your father's death and your mother's loneliness. What did you feel, and how did you react to the shouting that you heard next?

Sheila: I was looking at the woman and feeling sad, and then there was this angry shout. I just stood stock-still, like a statue, frozen with shock, wondering what it could be.

Debriefer: What did you feel, when you were standing there like a statue?

Sheila: Well, it was surprise at the noise, but I wondered what it was and thought that something was wrong.

Debriefer: What were you feeling?

Sheila: Shocked and frightened, I think, although I didn't know what was happening. Then I saw the robber walking out of the shop and was terrified when I saw the gun.

Debriefer: You were shocked and frightened. Did you believe it was happening?

Sheila: No. It was like a bad dream. It was as though I could see myself standing there and I was looking on. I think they call it an 'out-of-body experience'.

Debriefer: You couldn't believe it was happening and felt detached from your body?

Sheila: Yes. It was like a dream.

Debriefer: You said you were frightened. How frightened were you?

Sheila: I was terrified. Scared stiff. Then, when he pushed the old lady down I couldn't believe that anyone would do a thing like that. Then I thought he was going to kill me.

Debriefer: Let's go back a bit. You said you saw the robber and were immediately frightened. What was it about him that made you afraid?

Sheila: A lot of things, really. The way he looked and walked, and the gun.

Debriefer: You said earlier when you told the story that he looked aggressive and angry and that he walked with a sort of threatening confidence. You also said you could picture this when you closed your eyes. Does this still frighten you now?

Sheila: Well, not a lot. I can remember it and it is horrible, but the worst thing was his eyes. I told you they were like black holes staring at me as if to say, 'I'll get you if you try to stop me.' I just wanted to run away, but I couldn't move. I know that I began to shake with fear.

Debriefer: Because he was threatening you?

Sheila: Yes. It was the gun and his eyes.

Debriefer: His eyes were staring at you and he was pointing the gun. You said in the Facts Stage that you thought he might shoot you, but what did you feel when you saw the gun?

The debriefer then moves on to ask about her feelings when the robber pushed the old lady down.

Sheila: I felt frightened, but angry. How could he do that to an old woman? But also, what was he going to do to me?

The debriefer gradually moves through the story, taking each section of it and asking about the feelings and reactions associated with it, including the hidden reactions:

Debriefer: Sheila, at this stage you said you were terrified and couldn't move, and thought that he would kill you if you did anything to stop him. Do you remember having any other feelings at the time: anger, or helplessness?

Sheila: Oh, yes. I know I was frozen with fear, but inside
             I wanted to do something and was thinking, 'How
             can you do this to me when I am just shopping for
             my mother?' I was so angry, but I knew I couldn't
             do anything. I suppose I felt angry but helpless. I
             wanted to stop him, but knew I couldn't. It sounds
             stupid, but I just wish somebody like Clint East-
             wood had been there. We had seen *Dirty Harry* on
             the telly just a few days before.

Debriefer: You were very angry and frightened, but felt you
             were unable to do anything because of his threaten-
             ing behaviour and because of the gun. You men-
             tioned Clint Eastwood and wanting someone to do
             something. Is that what you felt at the time, or is
             it something you felt later or that you feel now?

Sheila: I don't know. I think it was around at the time, but
             it only came to me when he knocked the old lady
             down. It's certainly there now. I feel I want revenge
             for what he did to us. The police haven't caught
             him yet, but when they do I hope they put him away
             for a long time.

Debriefer: So you feel you want to get your own back in some
             way?

The debriefer makes his way through the story, continuing to
focus on specific reactions and dealing with each one in turn
before moving on to the next. He then asks:

'What was the worst thing for you about the incident?'

This is a wide-ranging question that is asked towards the end of
this section, before going on to look at positive reactions. It helps
the debriefee to focus on what her most difficult reactions are,
and can result in a strong upsurge of emotion.

Debriefer: We have looked at a number of reactions, but I
             would like to ask you another question. When you
             think of the whole incident, from beginning to end,

what was the very worst thing about it for you? Of all the reactions you had, what was the worst and what comes into your mind now?

The debriefer may have to wait for a while until the debriefee has thought about it—but she may have few doubts, or none at all.

Sheila: I can tell you without thinking about it. It's the fact that this swine could come into my life and ruin it, just like that, and there was nothing I could do. It's not just anger, but rage that he could have done this to me and taken away from me something important—control over my life. I know now that it could happen again. I just shake with rage sometimes.

Here rage, loss of control and vulnerability are Sheila's main emotions.

Experiences after the incident
The debriefer asks what feelings and reactions have emerged between the end of the incident and the Debriefing—this usually applies to the last three or four days, but will be longer in some cases.

Continuing with the armed robbery in the bank:

Debriefer: We talked through the incident to the point where you all went back to work the next day. There is a great deal of anger around and feelings of helplessness, even though you all coped well at the time. What feelings and reactions have you experienced, and which have been the most important for you between the incident and today?

The debriefer asks each person in turn.

Experiences now
He finishes by asking what feelings are around now.

Back to the armed robbery in the shopping centre:

Debriefer: Sheila, as you sit here now, what are your main feelings and reactions? You have said that the worst thing for you was the very real fear of being injured or killed, and that thought has come back to you since then. The incident happened more than three days ago. What do you feel now?

Sheila: That's difficult. I have so many feelings. I suppose the main one is anger—anger that it happened at all: anger that I was there in the first place; anger about the old lady; anger with myself for not being able to do anything; anger with my husband for not understanding. But most of all I'm angry with the man who did this to us. It's so unfair.

Debriefer: So, the main feeling is one of anger about a whole number of things, but mainly with the robber. You went through a very frightening experience and, in addition to anger, it has left you with a number of other feelings and reactions: from fear and helplessness, to realising your own vulnerability.

Positive reactions, lessons learned

The debriefer asks whether there have been any positive reactions since the incident and whether the debriefees have learned anything from it. But he should be aware that, especially after tragic incidents, there may be further anger or distress at being asked the question. Positive reactions or a sense of having learned something may not come until much later, if at all. Some may say they have learned that life is totally unpredictable, unfair or not worth living.

Debriefer: Sheila, now that the incident is over, I wonder if you feel that anything positive has come out of it. In spite of being frightened, angry and helpless, have you learned anything, good or bad? It could be about yourself, your life, your family, or anything.

Sheila: It sounds strange, but I think I know now that there are some rotten people around in the world, but also that not everyone is like that. There were some people who did help me and the old lady when it was over, and the nurses and doctors at the hospital, and the police officer, were just wonderful. I also know that my husband is all right, even if he doesn't understand what happened to me and how I feel. I was walking along thinking that everything was fine, when suddenly this happened. It made me think. Anyway, I know one thing I have learned: I am going back to the shop to buy that jumper. I don't care what happens—that man isn't going to ruin it all for me and for my mum's birthday.

The concentration on positive reactions eases the transition from the emotions and reactions of the Feelings Stage to the cognitive mode of the Future Stage.

2 The general method
This is identical to the general method used with sensory impressions. The debriefer takes a particular feeling or reaction, presents it to the debriefees in turn and asks them to relate it generally to the incident, not necessarily in chronological order of what happened. The questions should not be too general. If, for instance, the debriefer were to say, 'If we look at the whole incident, what feelings and reactions can you recall?', the debriefees would find it confusing and difficult to focus on. The technique is to take a specific feeling or reaction and ask about it generally:

Debriefer: I would like you all to think of the feelings and reactions that you associate with the incident, some of which have already been mentioned in the story. As you think of the robbery, what feelings, emotions and reactions did you experience? Let's take them in turn and begin with fear. Were you frightened? At what times were you afraid, and why? [He pauses.] Paul, let's start with you.

Paul: I was all right until I saw the robber. I knew straight away that something was wrong, but I wasn't sure what it was. He just looked strange, as I said earlier when I described him. Sort of shifty, but ready for aggro. Then, when he came up to the desk and pushed the note through, I knew immediately and I went all cold. Then he pushed the plastic bag through and I saw the gun. I just couldn't move, so how I gave him the money I'll never know. I was terrified, sort of frozen with fear. I put the money in the bag, gave it to him and my hands were shaking.

Debriefer: I know it sounds a strange question, but can you say why you were frightened?

Paul: Because I felt that I could be killed, that I would die. It was like being alone, even though there were others around me. Like being in an enormous fridge, cold and terrifying. I might never see my family again. And I can still feel this now. I'm alive, but I could be dead.

Debriefer: [He pauses, allowing the feeling to just be there.] You still feel this when you think about the robbery?

Paul: Yes. But I'm glad to be alive.

Debriefer: Any other times when you were afraid?

Paul: Well, in my car on the way home. I wasn't really frightened, just wary. I thought that he might be watching me or following me. I knew he wasn't, but that's how I felt.

Debriefer: What does this leave you with now?

Paul: I know it was a frightening experience and I should be grateful for being alive, which I am, but I woke up last night having a bad dream. I could see his face and the gun and I was frightened again. I woke up sweating like mad. My wife was upset, but we coped. I made a cup of tea and we just talked.

Debriefer: So, the fear is still around and came out in a dream. But, in spite of this, you say you coped, largely by talking to your wife. And you said you are grateful for being alive?

Paul: Oh, yes! I'm very lucky to have my wife and family and, in spite of the robbery, a job I enjoy. And, of course, my colleagues.

Debriefer: There seem to be both positive and negative feelings there for you; a bad experience and a very frightening one, but a good family, supportive colleagues and a good job. Thank you for that, Paul. Rachel, if I could ask you about fear. When were you afraid?

It is usually better to ask 'When were you afraid?' rather than 'Were you afraid?' It is easy for a person to answer the latter question by saying 'No', especially if defences are high. Asking 'When were you afraid?' gives permission for debriefees to believe that it is natural and normal to be frightened—or angry or guilty, or whatever.

Rachel: When I saw the gun. I heard the man come in, but, as I said earlier, I was busy with another customer so I didn't particularly look at him. It was only when I heard his voice asking Paul to hurry up that something rang bells and I looked to see what was happening. I knew it was a raid. I've been in one before and it was almost the same scene. I saw the man standing there looking at Paul and waving the gun around. I was terrified, just like Paul. But, I didn't go all cold or anything. It was as though I just went numb and became like a robot. I was very cool and calm and, although I was afraid, the fear seemed to go away. Until later, that is.

Debriefer: You were unaware of what was happening until you heard the voice. Did the voice frighten you at all, and can you recall it now?

Rachel: Not really, although it sounded threatening. I was only frightened when I saw the gun, but then the fear seemed to disappear. I felt totally calm, but numb.

Debriefer: You knew something was wrong and became afraid, but then the fear went away, you said, 'until later'?

Rachel:	Yes, when the robber left. I just started to shake with fear. My legs went wobbly and I thought I was going to faint. That's when I turned to Paul and threw my arms around him.
Debriefer:	You found that helpful?
Rachel:	Yes, I did. I would have fallen over if I hadn't done it.
Paul:	I thought you were hugging me to help me! I didn't realise you were scared at the time, like me.

The debriefer then explores fear with the other members of staff, and moves on to look at other feelings and reactions, asking people to relate these to the place in the incident where they occurred. He also asks about covert feelings and about physical reactions. Then, as with the specific method, he asks:

'What was the worst thing for you about the incident?'

Experiences after the incident and now

The debriefer asks what reactions have occurred between the end of the incident and the Debriefing and about what feelings, emotions and reactions are being experienced now.

Positive reactions, lessons learned

As with the specific method, and bearing in mind that this can be threatening and inappropriate after some incidents, the debriefer begins the move to the cognitive, Future Stage mode by asking about positive reactions. Back to the bank robbery Debriefing:

Debriefer:	I would like you all to think of any positive reactions that you might have had during the incident and that you have now. Have there been any positive reactions, and have you learned anything? What about you, Paul?
Paul:	I don't know, it was a frightening experience so I'm not sure if I've learned anything. I was OK at the beginning and looking forward to going to the cinema with my wife that evening. Then everything

changed. One thing I do know is that I'm grateful to my colleagues and for the support they have given me. I was feeling numb and shocked by what had happened, and Rachel just came up to me, put her arms around me and held me. It was good and I felt a lot of the fear and tension going out of me. The smell of the perfume also helped.

Debriefer: What about when the incident was over?

Paul: When the police came? I knew we were all safe. I just said out loud, 'Thank God for that!' I also felt strange when I went home. Mind you, I did burst into tears with relief when I saw my wife and children. I was so grateful to be alive.

Debriefer: What do you think about it now?

Paul: Well, it was very frightening, but I think that we are stronger for it as a team. At least, I feel we are. We all coped very well and I am pleased about that. Also, I'm grateful for my life as it is now and for my family.

Debriefer: So, in spite of the robbery you have had positive reactions and say that you have learned to appreciate your colleagues and your family. Thank you for that. Rachel, what about you? Have you had any positive feelings or learned anything?

Rachel: Yes. I was frightened at the time, but I was in a good mood before it started. Things have been going well in my life and I am moving soon to another branch as assistant manager. I know I was afraid, but I also know that I coped well, and so did the others. I'm glad I could help Paul, but he doesn't know how much that hug also helped me. I saw that he had faced the robber and I just stood there unable to do anything. When he had gone, I just ran to Paul and hugged him. It was more for myself than for him.

Debriefer: So, you were feeling good at the beginning and then were very frightened, but the contact between you and Paul helped you to cope. Also, you believe that

	you all coped very well and supported each other.
Rachel:	Yes. And I know that as an assistant manager I will understand how these incidents can affect people and I think this will help me and the rest of my staff.

The debriefer then asks other debriefees in turn, and affirms what they say by reflecting and confirming any positive reactions and any suggestions that they have learned something about themselves or about life.

Ending the Feelings Stage

The debriefer gives a short summary of the incident and of its effect on the debriefees, talks about any positive reactions or lessons that have emerged, and asks if there are any questions.

Debriefer:	You have all been through a difficult experience and there have been many different reactions to what happened. You felt shock and fear and numbness and a sense that it wasn't really happening, followed by anger at what this man did to you by taking away the feeling of being in control of your own lives. There are a number of sensory reactions such as sights and images that come back to you, and smells and sounds which conjure up the incident. These can still trigger reactions for you, but you know where they come from and that they are the result of being involved in the robbery.
	However, there have also been some positive things for you: you feel that you can depend on each other more and that you are stronger both as a team and as individuals. You coped and, even if there are still some difficult reactions to be dealt with, you see your families and friends in a new way and you say you are grateful for your lives. Thank you for being so honest and open in telling your stories. Unless there are any questions, we'll move on to look at the future.

12   Stage 3: The Future

In the first two stages the debriefees worked through the facts of their stories, operating in a cognitive mode, to the feelings, where they concentrated on emotions and reactions. In Stage 3 they look at the present and prepare for the future, and the task of the debriefer is to take them into a cognitive mode again. He does this in three steps, or sections:

1   *Normalisation* is concerned with showing that, whatever the debriefees have experienced, their reactions are normal.
2   *Information* is given about possible future reactions.
3   *Support* considers their own personal resources and at who and what are available to provide help in the future, should they need it.

The purpose is also to offer what Dyregrov calls 'anticipatory guidance', so that the debriefees will be prepared for further reactions, should any occur. The three sections involve the debriefer often doing most of the talking, yet allowing time for questions and some discussion.

1   NORMALISATION

The debriefer talks about the normality of reactions to traumatic events and gives examples from his own experience. The debriefees are encouraged to see themselves as:

> normal people who have experienced an abnormal event and who are having normal reactions.

However, the debriefer should be prepared for some to see this statement as condescending, trite or unhelpful, and to react with anger or resentment. It sounds right, but it may not feel right, because although reactions *are* usually normal they can be very distressing and disturbing, and this needs to be acknowledged. Someone may retort:

'It's all right for you to say that my reactions are normal, but they don't feel normal. They feel terrible.'

The object of this section is to help to allay any fears on the part of the debriefees that they are going mad or are stupid or weak or inadequate. Reactions are affirmed as genuine and real—and normal; and the debriefer should put this in a way that is accept-able to the individual or group. The preamble to this stage leads on from the ending of the Feelings Stage:

Debriefer: We now move on to the third stage, where we look to the future. You have all been through a very frightening incident, and experienced many differ-ent kinds of reaction, from fear and helplessness to unreality and anger, but it is important for you to know and believe that whatever reactions you had at the time or have had since then, or that you still have now, are normal. You are normal people who have experienced an abnormal event and, even if some of them are disturbing, your feelings, emo-tions and reactions, for you, are normal. They are the ways in which your mind and body cope with what you have been through. No matter how dis-tressing or disturbing these reactions may be, they are not signs of weakness or inadequacy. You are not stupid or incapable because you experience them. Anger, helplessness and fear are natural reac-tions to what you have been through and, in a way, you would probably be abnormal if you didn't experience them. What should be helpful is that you have already talked in detail about your reactions

and, hopefully, will feel able to talk to someone in
the future if you need to do so.

Would you like to make any comments about
any of your reactions or ask any questions about
what I have said?

The debriefer then deals with any questions or problems raised.
The debriefees may talk about feelings, emotions or reactions,
some of which they may not have mentioned before, and these
can be an appropriate link with the next section.

2 INFORMATION: POSSIBLE FUTURE REACTIONS

Now the debriefer talks about the possibility of other reactions
occurring in the future, but does not in any way suggest that they
will happen; this should not result in anyone thinking:

'I haven't had that yet. Perhaps I'll have it tomorrow?'

This is a necessary caution, because debriefers have been accused
of trying to convince debriefees that they 'owe themselves a
problem'. Although debriefers are aware of what reactions there
might be and that some debriefees may hide their feelings quite
successfully, they do not conduct Debriefings with preconceived
ideas of what reactions there will be. Debriefers should only deal
with what is present as a result of the incident. Problems deriving
from other events and experiences, both past and present, will
often be raised: these are important, and will be acknowledged
by the debriefer. But no attempt will be made to counsel or
debrief in relation to such problems.

In this section, the debriefer gives a presentation on possible
future reactions, including some that have already been mentioned
and some that have not. He takes a selection of reactions appropriate to the incident and explains that they can be resurrected by
something external or, on the other hand, materialise without
obvious trigger or warning. These reactions are discussed in
Chapter 2 in relation to responses to trauma, and the debriefer

should be able to talk about them and give examples. He should present the information in a manner that suggests that most people will recover naturally within a short time. The main reactions to be considered are:

Intrusive thoughts and images

Debriefer: Intrusive thoughts and images can come at any time: for instance, when you are relaxing or reading, at work or at home; when trying to sleep; when walking down the street, or when not doing anything in particular. A thought or image from or about the incident can come into your mind, gradually or suddenly, and cause a reaction. Sometimes these thoughts or images are of a person or of something significant, even though you may have been unaware of him or her or it at the time. They can be triggered by or accompanied by sensory impressions—a smell, a sight, a sound, a feeling or a taste—and can be very frightening and disturbing. Two of you have said that you keep seeing the robber's eyes and that this frightens you. Images like this may come at certain times, but should gradually be less disturbing and eventually go away.

Heightened feelings of anxiety and vulnerability

Debriefer: You were put into a situation in which a man took away your feeling of being in control, and some of you felt anxious and vulnerable. Feeling that we are in control of our lives is very important, and when we lose it, even for a short time, feelings of disorientation, confusion and insecurity can set in. This can affect relationships with others as well as feelings about ourselves. The feelings that you have experienced may come back again, but are the result of what this man did to you.

Irritability and anger

Debriefer: Some of you may feel irritated by trivial things at home, at work or elsewhere—irritated with yourself, your partner, your children, or anyone at all. The children arguing, a partner nagging, colleagues or pressure at work—all of these, in the aftermath of such an incident, can cause strong reactions, from resentment or exasperation to rage. Little things that normally wouldn't bother you can grow out of proportion. One man who had been in an armed robbery flared up at the slightest thing and, when they went out to a restaurant or party, his wife would ask him to control himself and not lose his temper with the waiter. Again, reactions like these are the normal response to what you have been through.

Difficulty in concentrating or in making decisions

Debriefer: You might experience difficulty in thinking straight, in concentrating at work or in reading a book or newspaper, or in making even simple decisions. Things that others consider important may seem trivial when compared with what you have experienced, so your response may be 'Why bother to do this?' or 'It doesn't matter.' Some people find that they lose confidence or can't concentrate on driving or operating a machine, but normal functions usually return after a short time.

Inability to show feelings or emotions

Debriefer: You may find it difficult to express to people how you feel—especially to those you love—not just about the incident, but about your life in general. This can happen for a number of reasons: some will not want others to ask them about what happened

and so will withdraw from their families, friends or
colleagues; feeling vulnerable may result in self-
isolation in order not to feel threatened, and you
might at the very least wish to be on your own more
than usual; the experience you have undergone can
itself be isolating because others will not or cannot
understand, no matter how hard they try, and you
may feel that they are pushing you away. On the
other hand, they may feel that you are pushing *them*
away.

Dreams and nightmares

Debriefer: You may find that you are having disturbing
dreams, or nightmares, which can result from suppressing your emotions or feelings or from denying
that the experience was disturbing. Perhaps what
happens is that, when you are relaxing or asleep,
your defences are lowered, permitting these experiences to emerge in this way. Talking about them to
someone you trust can help.

Changes in thoughts, beliefs, life view or behaviour

Debriefer: Some of you may find that changes occur in the
way you feel or think about life and about your-
selves. There can be changes in beliefs, whether in
attitudes and opinions or in relation to religion or
your view of the world. You may react to different
things in different ways from usual. A desire to
change your life may well affect relationships, partners, jobs or lifestyle. This can be disturbing for
you and for those around you. Others may say to
you, 'You're not the same person you were.' The
answer to this is, of course, that you are indeed not
the same person. You have been through a terrifying
incident which is now part of your experience and

have learned more about yourself, about others and about life. So although you are still you, you in some ways are a new person.

The debriefer may point out many other possible reactions, based on his knowledge of the incident and on the ways in which the debriefees have reacted, and depending on the time available.

Re-experiencing, avoidance behaviour and arousal

The debriefer might now mention the three major reactions of re-experiencing, avoidance behaviour and arousal, all associated with PTS and the development of PTSD, and give brief examples of each.

Debriefer: You may not experience any of these in a dramatic way—although you have mentioned some of them—but I thought I should talk about them because they are typical and natural reactions which some people have to what you have experienced.

The first is *re-experiencing*. You might be any-where—at work or at home, for instance—and begin to feel angry or upset or irritated. It might just come 'out of the blue', or it could be triggered by something external. For example, a man who had been mugged was incensed whenever he saw examples of similar violence on television. A sight, a sound, a touch, a taste or a smell might cause old feelings to be resurrected.

Another common experience is *avoidance behaviour*, when you feel that you don't want to be reminded of the incident and try to avoid talking about it. A woman involved in an armed robbery in a bank found it difficult to go back behind her till the next day and asked if she could be given some other work until she felt able to cope. Some say that they are a bit withdrawn, feel isolated for a while, or think that nobody understands how they feel; or find being with others, even their families, difficult.

The third experience is *arousal*, in which the nervous system seems to become very sensitive and you react to ordinary things in a different way from usual. For example, a door banging, a car backfiring, or just being touched by somebody can cause a strong reaction—called an 'exaggerated startle response'. Or you may feel that you cannot stand the noise of the children at home or the atmosphere at work, and you become irritated and want to get away.

These are all normal reactions, but they can be disturbing. If they happen to you, try to see where they come from and identify where they belong in your experience. They are not your fault, but the result of what you have been through.

These reactions are discussed in Chapter 2.

Persistent reactions

The debriefer explains that if any emotional reactions or feelings persist or become worse, then the option of getting help should be considered—that is, help via talking to a member of the family or friend, or to a professional. Then, without alarming the debriefees, and remembering that some may feel vulnerable or threatened, he outlines possible developments that would prompt thoughts of seeking help:

● *If reactions do not decrease after 4–6 weeks* Normally, reactions decrease in the first three to four weeks, but the time frame is usually much longer when the trauma is caused by a death or other major loss, or after involvement in a particularly terrifying or horrific incident.

● *If reactions increase over time* Any reactions should decrease as time passes, and most people will be back to their normal functioning within a short while—some within a few hours or days. Some, though, may take longer; and there may be others who experience no disturbing reactions at the time, but may do so months or even years after the incident.

• *If there is loss of function or ability* This can occur at home or at work, in personal relationships or in any other aspect of life. Some may experience a reduced ability to concentrate or to express or feel emotions (see pages 223–4), or an inability to carry out skills or simple tasks that have been previously learned. Debriefees may feel lethargic and listless and not want to do anything.

• *If marked personality changes occur* Some may notice in themselves or in others that changes are taking place in character or in personality: the quiet mouse becomes the roaring lion, or vice versa; someone who has always seemed happy-go-lucky becomes depressed or remorseful or cynical; another displays inappropriate anger or aggression, or develops agoraphobia, claustrophobia or obsessional or compulsive behaviour; a usually gregarious person withdraws from involvement with others. Individuals may not be aware of these changes taking place in themselves, but a group can provide mutual monitoring.

The main message of this section is that debriefees should not be afraid to ask for help if they need it, and that group members can provide mutual support.

Debriefer: You should all be aware of the possibility that reactions might recur, or you might have reactions that you have not had before. There are certain guidelines I can give you. First, if you find that you are having reactions that do not decrease within four to six weeks or that increase as time passes, then think of asking for help. Second, if you find that you are losing concentration or have more difficulty than normal in making decisions, or you feel that your personality is changing, ask for help. It's no good, if you feel that you are struggling along, thinking 'I'll manage—it will soon go away', because it might not. If this happens, look for someone to talk to. I don't mean that you should spy on each other, but you do know each other well and work closely together. If you think that someone is not coping, then have the courage to approach him or her in private, and ask if you can help.

This may lead to comments or questions.

Coping strategies

Coping strategies used during an incident are discussed in Chapter 3, and some of them are continued after the event. Here the concern is with strategies for coping in the future. The debriefer should be able to provide guidance for those who ask what they can do about certain feelings and reactions that they still have. In some cases referral to a doctor, occupational health nurse or professional stress or trauma counsellor may be called for.

Strategies that the debriefer might suggest to the debriefees:

- To accept that their reactions are normal; to realise that any feelings and reactions belong in the incident, come from that experience, and are not signs of weakness.
- To find someone they can trust and with whom they can share their story and feelings.
- To carry on their lives as normal and, if possible, not to make any major changes in the early stages.
- To remember that a healthy diet and regular exercise are important.
- To look again at what has happened to them and try to see it from a different perspective—to try to find something positive in what they have experienced.
- To try relaxation techniques, using CDs, cassette tapes or videos—available from major high street stores or through the doctor, occupational health nurse or counsellor.
- Not to be afraid of reactions; to allow them to emerge. It can help to express emotions alone and in private, or with someone you can trust.

Even if these strategies are not discussed, debriefees should be asked how they have coped since the incident. The debriefer can begin by asking what unhelpful things have happened and then about helpful things. This can result in discussion and should lead on to the next section, which looks at support.

Debriefer: It is now four days since the incident, and I wonder how you feel you have coped. I would like to ask you two questions. First, what things have happened that you have found unhelpful, originating either in other people or in yourself? Second, what has helped you to cope, and what have you done in order to cope?

Let's look at the first question. What has happened that has been unhelpful? It may be the attitudes, words or actions of others, or something you yourself have done. John, perhaps you could begin.

This may be directed at each person in turn, or posed as a general question leading to a short discussion.

Hand-outs
The debriefer should have available leaflets or booklets on traumatic reactions and coping strategies. Many organisations such as banks, building societies, the police, hospitals and aid agencies produce booklets relating to the specific needs of their employees. An excellent leaflet is published by the Red Cross for general use. It is better to give these at the end of the Debriefing, with the hand-outs on support agencies.

3 SUPPORT

In this section, the debriefer asks the debriefees to look at what support is available for them. This is like dropping a stone into a pond: with the individual at the centre, the ripples spread out to include family and friends, the group, the internal support available from the employer organisation, and outside agencies.

Personal support
Each person is asked who he has talked to most since the incident, and whether he feels he can continue to talk to them should he

need to do so. The debriefer's aim is for each debriefee to identify someone he or she can talk to and who can listen. Back to the bank robbery Debriefing:

Debriefer: I would like you to think about support and about who or what has helped you to cope since the incident. Think of someone you have talked to, or could talk to, about what you have experienced. [He pauses.] Who have you spoken to who has been helpful? Paul?

Paul: Well, my wife has been very supportive and understanding and I can tell her anything. I know she has a job and the kids to look after and I don't want to over-burden her, but I think that I couldn't have a better person to support me.

Debriefer: That's very positive for you, Paul. And you feel that you can still talk to her if you need to?

Paul: Yes, I do.

Debriefer: Rachel, what about you?

Rachel: You know I mentioned earlier that I live with my parents? Well, my dad doesn't understand and has never mentioned it. He's of the old stiff-upper-lip school and just expects me to get on with my life, so I can't talk to him. My mum is different and I can talk to her. We just sat down the night it happened and talked and talked and she was wonderful. I know that I can tell her anything, so I'm all right.

Debriefer: Thank you Rachel. Diana, what about you?

Diana: Well, it's a bit difficult as I live on my own. When I got home afterwards, I was all by myself in the flat.

Debriefer: What did you do in order to cope? Was there anybody you talked to?

Diana: Well, first I just got on with making something to eat and listened to the radio and watched TV. Fortunately I have a sister not far away, and I rang her and she came round straight away to see me.

> Like Rachel and her mum, we just talked and I
> know I can ring her if I need to. In fact, I've phoned
> her every evening since then.

If someone says that he or she has nobody, he or she is asked
who might be available.

Debriefer: Diana, you've said that there isn't anyone for you
to talk to and you don't get on with your family.
Is there anybody you feel you could trust, perhaps
a neighbour or friend?

Diana: Well, I suppose I could talk to Ruth. She's an old
friend. I've known her a long time, but we've not
been in touch recently. Mind you, I know somebody
from this group who I could talk to, but I'd rather
not say who it is. We both know, and that's sufficient.

The person that the debriefee pinpoints will usually be a partner, spouse, parent, relative, friend or colleague, or a clergyman,
a GP or other professional that he or she knows. For some it can
be a pet or even a photograph of a loved one. The debriefer
should make a note if there is anyone who feels there is nobody
they can talk to, for possible referral when the Debriefing is over.

In a one-to-one Debriefing the procedure is the same, with the
debriefer trying to identify who is available to help.

Group support
The debriefer looks at what support the group can offer:

Debriefer: I'm wondering what support you can give to each
other as a team?

Debriefing usually results in an increase in team solidarity.
The group may suggest having coffee together so that they can
talk, or that they should all go out for a meal or to a pub for a
drink. A comment frequently made by debriefees at this stage is
that they are all aware that the Debriefing has strengthened them
as a team and that they can support each other. If a manager is

present, it may be suggested that the team meet once a week to discuss how they are coping.

Organisational support

The debriefer outlines what organisational support is available. Debriefees are normally informed during their training of who and what is available from their organisation—this can include managers, supervisors, human resources and occupational health staff, welfare and personnel departments, chaplains, counsellors, peer supporters, consultant psychiatrists and psychologists and people available through employee assistance programmes. At this point individuals may comment on their previous experience of these sources of support.

External resources

The group is then asked about external resources and agencies, and people known to them who may be able to help. The debriefer needs to mention here agencies that may not be known to the debriefees, such as medical and chaplaincy services, GPs, Victim Support, Cruse, Relate, Citizens' Advice Bureaux, Rape Crisis lines and rape centres, the Samaritans and the Compassionate Friends. He should know which organisations are available locally and have with him leaflets listing names and telephone numbers of appropriate people and agencies.

THE AFTERMATH

Photographs and identity parades

After some incidents, especially where there has been criminal activity, debriefers will need to talk about the possibility of identity parades, or of being asked to look at photographs of suspects or to help construct faces from an identikit or computer or with an artist.

The debriefer should know the answers in advance, but he should nonetheless ask the debriefees whether there have been any identity parades, or whether they have been asked to look at photographs or to work with identikits. If any of this *has* already happened, it should be discussed; if it might happen or is about to, the debriefer should remind people that the experience may unleash intense emotions. As already mentioned, the police are usually very sensitive to the ways in which people may react— but not always:

> Two days after an armed robbery in a building society, a plain-clothes police officer walked into the branch and, without saying who he was, threw down some photographs on to the counter in front of the young cashier who had faced the robber. 'Is that him?' he asked. The cashier was immediately terrified and began to scream. She was totally unprepared for the sudden appearance of a stranger confronting her with photographs of the suspect.

> After another armed robbery, a police officer wanted to take the woman who had faced the robber to the local police station to make a statement and to look at photographs. He insisted that she go alone and, although the manager protested strongly, she was taken off to the station where she felt terrified, isolated and threatened. The manager asked if she could be accompanied by a friend, but the police officer refused.

These are extreme and, hopefully, rare examples. But those involved certainly often *do* feel very vulnerable, and seeing the criminal again, or even just a photograph, can result in re-traumatisation or in re-experiencing reactions. Not all identity parades are the same, so police should be asked to explain what form they will take.

Court cases

Court cases, too, can be very threatening, and can result in severe traumatic reactions in victims and witnesses. Sometimes they do not take place until months, or even years, after the incident, and those involved are often unprepared for the emotional reactions they experience—some have reported feeling that they, rather than the suspect, were in the dock. The very fact of the defence going about its normal business of questioning the evidence and attempting to discredit it can be difficult for witnesses and others, who will already be feeling vulnerable and anxious. Even where a suspect pleads guilty, people can still experience disturbing reactions.

Inquests and inquiries

Debriefees should also be prepared for any inquests or inquiries that may be necessary. These can be as traumatic as the incident, especially where there exists the possibility of apportioning blame in the case of deaths or injuries.

In all these situations, debriefers should ask debriefees to:

- Insist on being accompanied by a family member, colleague or friend.
- Find out where the procedure(s) will take place.
- Ask what form they will take (photographs, slides, drawings?).
- Ask who will be present.
- Be prepared to experience disturbing, possibly traumatic, reactions, even if they are just attending as a witness or friend.
- Be prepared if they have to give evidence and, if necessary, seek advice from the police, a solicitor or a lawyer.

All should consider the usefulness of talking to a professional counsellor or therapist after the experience.

Hospital and home visits

When people have been injured, especially family members, friends or colleagues, it is usually a good idea for them to receive visits, get-well cards or flowers. Where strangers are injured, people sometimes feel the need to visit them either because they have shared a common experience or because they feel some responsibility. Whether the victim is at home or in hospital, visits and any other kind of communication can often help everyone to cope better, but may be difficult because of uncertainty about how individuals will react.

Funerals and memorial services

Non-family members may have reservations about attending funerals or memorial services for the victim(s) of an incident, feeling that they may not be welcome.

> The driver and one passenger were killed when their car skidded off the road. Another passenger survived, and was taken to hospital. The occupants of the car following saw what happened. They stopped, attempted resuscitation and rescue and called the police and ambulance. They did not know those who died, but during the Debriefing they asked whether they should contact the relatives of the dead or send cards or letters, and expressed a wish to attend the funerals, which were to be held locally. After some discussion it was resolved that they would make contact with the relatives and, depending on the outcome, decide later whether to attend the funerals.

Here, the witnesses felt that they wanted to express their sadness and condolences. The concerns raised by this incident are common to many events involving strangers:

> 'Should we contact the relatives of those who died?' 'How should we do this—by telephone, letter or personal visit?'
>
> 'If we do visit them, will they think that we were involved in, or to blame for, the accident? Although there was nothing we could do, will they blame us for not having saved the victims' lives? Might they think that we are calling only because we feel guilty?'
>
> 'We want to attend the funerals, but will we be welcome? Will it help the relatives, and us? Should we send flowers and a card?'
>
> 'We want to visit the person in hospital, but will he resent our visit? Will it help him or make him feel worse to be reminded of the accident, by seeing us? We did comfort him at the scene, but he was unconscious so he would not remember us.'

Similarly, someone who witnessed a mugging, rape or robbery might feel guilty for not having been able to help, but wish to contact the victim(s); in the case of a suicide at work, colleagues might wish to contact the family but feel that they might be blamed; a woman whose husband has returned safely from a war might want to visit the wife of one of his friends who was killed, but feel guilty because her husband is alive and fear that she might be resented or become the focus for anger or grief; a driver who has run over and killed a stranger might not know what actions to take.

When the Debriefing is over, the debriefer may need to liaise with senior colleagues to discuss the involvement of those who are to take part in any of the procedures described above or who might need help, advice or support.

Stage 3 should help debriefees to move into the future with hope and confidence, taking with them the awareness of their experiences, some understanding of their reactions, and a knowledge of where they can go if they need help.

The debriefer then moves on to conclude the Debriefing.

13   Ending the Debriefing

Each debriefer should find a way of ending the Debriefing which suits both his own style and the people he is debriefing. However he may do it, the aims are the same: to show that the Debriefing is over; to allow each person to feel that he or she has achieved something and to make a final statement; where necessary, to provide opportunity for referral.

ANY QUESTIONS OR COMMENTS?

The debriefer tells everyone that the Debriefing is almost over, and asks if there are any final questions, or if there is anything more that the debriefees would like to say (for instance, something that has just been remembered).

FINAL STATEMENTS

The debriefer states that each member of the Debriefing will be asked to make a final statement, if she wishes to do so—about how she feels or what she is thinking now. With a group, final statements are made not to the debriefer, but to everyone present. The debriefer can use the usual method of asking around the group, with each person replying in turn; or the group can be addressed generally, with people responding as and when they wish. As throughout the Debriefing, nobody should be allowed to dominate the group, and everyone who wishes to do so should be given an opportunity to reply.

Debriefer: We are now almost at the end of the Debriefing, and in order to round it off I would like you all to focus on how you feel now and what is going through your minds. How do you feel, and what are you thinking as you sit here, having been through the Debriefing? [He pauses.] I would like each one of you, in turn, to make a final statement, not to me, but to the group—to everyone here. You can say whatever you wish, and I will not make any comments about what you say. If you don't wish to make a statement, just shake your head or let me know in some other way.

Members of the group can reply in anything from *one word* to a general statement. For instance:

Debriefer: I would like you to say to the whole group just one word that describes what you are feeling and thinking now as you sit here. John, let's start with you. Just one word.

The same can be done with *two words*, *a one-sentence statement*, *a two-sentence statement* or *a general statement*:

Debriefer: Think about how you feel now and what you are thinking, and make a general statement to the group about it. I don't expect you to make a long speech, but just to say what is going through your mind as you sit here, now that the Debriefing is almost over.

Statements should be allowed to stand, usually without the debriefer commenting. If someone feels that it has all been a waste of time, the debriefer should not attempt to defend the Debriefing process. Whatever is said should be accepted and, where appropriate, acknowledged.

In one-word statements, words such as 'tired', 'exhausted', 'sad', 'angry', 'happy', 'comfortable', 'vulnerable' and 'threatened' are common; some may say that they do not feel anything and a few will not wish to respond—although this is unusual. As was noted earlier, the debriefer should not be unduly concerned about a lack of response, because the Debriefing process encourages silent Debriefing, where people internalise the process and debrief themselves just by listening and being present.

Typical general responses:

'I would like to thank everybody for being so honest and I am glad I came. I wasn't sure at the beginning, but I think it has been very helpful. I feel comfortable and am looking forward to getting home.'

'I didn't know what to expect and I must say that I have found it difficult and sometimes painful. However, I do believe that it has helped me and it was good to hear that others have felt like I have. I thought I was the only one, but now I know that I am not alone in what I feel.'

'I just want to say that I am grateful for being here, and that's all.'

'It has been very interesting for me, and I must say that I feel absolutely exhausted. But I think it has helped, and I am glad to know that we all have each other for support.'

'Just to say that I do feel much better.'

'I have found it very difficult and I'm not sure yet how I feel, but I think I am OK.'

'I don't want to say anything, but I'm OK too, I think.'

'I'm shattered.'

'I don't know yet. I still feel a bit shaky and uncertain.'

'I can't say much except that I don't know how I feel. Probably a bit overwhelmed.'

'I just want to get on with my life.'

'I still feel awful.'

The Debriefer should remember that in the Introduction to the Debriefing the debriefees were told that some might feel worse, so no one should be surprised if this is the case. If the debriefer does make any comments, they should be supportive and reflect and acknowledge what has been said. If somebody breaks down and cries, the debriefer asks someone from the group to offer him support; if he says that he feels worse, the debriefer might make a point of speaking to him afterwards to ask him whether he would like further support. Strong reactions can indicate that a person needs help but, on the other hand, the fact that he is expressing how he feels may signal that he is coping.

In a one-to-one Debriefing, the debriefee is asked to make a statement *without* particularly directing his words at the debriefer. The latter avoids any suggestion that 'Tell *me* how you feel' is what he is saying, because this may imply that the two of them are engaged in a counselling session.

Debriefer: Sheila, now that the Debriefing is over I would like you to say something about how you are feeling and what you are thinking now—not to me, but generally. You can say one word or several, or a few sentences, if you wish.

THANKING THE DEBRIEFEES

The debriefer thanks the debriefees for taking part. He ends by saying that the Debriefing is now over, that refreshments are being served (if appropriate), and that he will be available should anyone wish to talk or ask any further questions.

Debriefer: I would like to thank you all for being here and taking part, and I am grateful for your involvement and for being so honest. It's not an easy process, and we have been together a long time now. I expect most of you are very tired and looking forward to moving on to whatever you have planned next. Tea and coffee are provided in the next room, and I hope that you can stay. I will be staying for a cup of tea, and if any of you wish to speak to me or ask any questions you can do so then. I will be having a word with your manager afterwards, but won't be discussing anything personal from the Debriefing. You raised some practical matters such as the noisy security camera, and you have agreed that I should raise this with him. If there is time and you are here later, I will be around to say a final farewell.

The debriefees can then return to work, stay for tea or coffee, go home or do whatever else they may want to.

Some debriefers shake hands with everyone as they leave and, occasionally, because emotions have been high, debriefees may hug each other—and, sometimes, the debriefer!

REFERRAL

Jeffrey Mitchell and George Everly describe Debriefing as a preventive, not a cure, for traumatic reactions (Mitchell and Everly 1995). They make it quite clear that when a Debriefing is concluded it is not over, and that it should not be seen as an end in itself—although this might be the case if everyone is coping well and is content to move on. The problem is that nobody can tell, even from a Debriefing, how anyone may react in the future. Whenever possible, the debriefer should spend some time informally with the group after the Debriefing. This may take the form of a general chat over refreshments, but some individuals may ask if they can speak to him separately (and may have already intimated in the Debriefing that they would like to).

During the Debriefing it may have become obvious to the debriefer that some people are finding it difficult to cope: they were silent and looked—and still look—angry, uncomfortable, sad or depressed; they were, or are, distressed, and they may have cried and expressed a wish to see the debriefer afterwards; they looked, and still look, threatened, and they may have said in their final statements that they felt like this; they were heavily defended against replying, and were hostile or distant. Some may have mentioned other events which have been resurrected by the Debriefing: a bereavement or other loss, or a major life change or previous traumatic incident.

But the debriefer has to guard against assuming that those who are, or who look, distressed are those most in need of help. The people who seem to be unaffected may well be coping admirably; or, conversely, they may be suppressing and denying their feelings and reactions and needing to talk, but will not admit it. Crying may be one debriefee's way of coping; she feels better for having done so, and needs nothing further. When chatting informally after the Debriefing, the debriefer bears in mind especially those who have found the procedure difficult. He asks them how they are coping, and affirms the availability of support; and a few individuals may need to be referred for advice or counselling. Mitchell states that, in his experience, referrals for therapy are rare (as low as 1–3 per cent), but some claim that the rate in major disasters and other serious incidents can be as high as 50 per cent for both immediate victims and rescuers. In my experience Debriefings rarely entail referral for counselling as a direct result of the incident, but referral is occasionally necessary for other traumatic experiences, both past and present, that have been resurrected by the Debriefing.

POST-DEBRIEFING PROCEDURE

Future meetings

Debriefees occasionally ask to meet with the debriefer at some later date, and this can be arranged when the Debriefing is over. Whether with individuals or with groups, this meeting may be for advice, for counselling or for referral, or for checking out reactions and reinforcing the Debriefing process.

Meetings with senior personnel

Since not all senior personnel know about post-traumatic stress reactions or about the Debriefing process, the debriefer should, wherever possible, have an informal talk with the person responsible for the individual or group. Here are the main points to consider:

● *Is a mini-Debriefing with this senior person appropriate?* If she has not attended the Debriefing, this meeting can turn into a useful mini-Debriefing in which she talks about where she was when the incident took place, how and when she found out and reacted, and what she feels about it now. Similarly, if she asks what the procedure is about, this too may lead to a mini-Debriefing, or to a counselling session: on one occasion, when a senior manager raised the problem of his own marriage, the debriefer referred him to a counsellor. A senior person who did attend the Debriefing might talk about feelings and reactions that she was unable to mention in the Debriefing, with junior personnel present.

● *Confidential matters should not be discussed without the permission of debriefees.* The debriefer should discuss with seniors any matters mentioned by the debriefees that cannot be treated as confidential because of the implications either for themselves or for others—but always with the knowledge and co-operation of the debriefees.

● *What security matters need to be mentioned that have been raised in the Debriefing? Will some action be taken about them?* Practical matters arising from the Debriefing should be discussed and handed on, hopefully for some action to be taken. In the case of banks, building societies, post-offices, petrol stations, shops and similar premises, the debriefer can raise matters, such as security, which have been mentioned in the Debriefing, so that new or improved measures can be adopted and implemented.

● *The importance of monitoring members of staff over the next few weeks or months.* Where there is concern over individual or group reactions, the debriefer should talk about the need for good monitoring of staff responses, and about the availability of advice or help. Where necessary, leaflets or booklets about post-traumatic reactions can be given to seniors. Whenever possible, after any meeting with seniors, debriefers should make their way around the workplace and informally say goodbye to them, as they would after any other Debriefing.

Some organisations use ongoing assessment as part of a wider response following Debriefings sometimes at three- or six-month intervals.

Reports and records
Debriefers need to keep personal records of Debriefings, but they should be treated as confidential and kept secure. No personal reports should be given to the employer organisation without the permission of those involved. If reports *are* given, those involved may have the right to read them. Records should include:

- Date, time and place of the Debriefing.
- A list of those who attended, with their contact addresses and telephone numbers.
- A short summary of the incident, with details of the length and degree of trauma and whether or not violence or weapons were used.
- A list of the main reactions and topics discussed: feelings, emotions and physical reactions.
- Details of any practical suggestions or recommendations made by debriefees and handed on to senior personnel.
- Names and contact numbers of senior personnel and internal support services.
- Details of the referral system used.
- Any general or personal comments.

Supervision
The final task of debriefers is to ensure that their own needs are met. Debriefing involves spending many hours with debriefees, which requires the intensive use of personal skills and resources and can be exhausting. Debriefers will absorb and reflect many of the feelings generated in the Debriefing, as well as experiencing their own emotional reactions. At times they will feel that they have not done their best, while at others they will feel a sense of achievement. Whatever their reactions, personal supervision— and, where possible, group supervision with other debriefers— is essential. It should provide physical and psychological support, help to maintain professional standards and provide further training opportunities; and involve checking out methods of working and sharing ideas and experiences.

Where the Debriefing has been conducted by people trained within the organisation, they should report to their Debriefing organiser that a Debriefing has taken place. The organiser should then check that personal and group supervision of all debriefers takes place regularly. Those who work independently may consider either looking for or organising group supervision with other debriefers in their area.

14 Using the Three-stage Revised Debriefing Model

The three-stage Debriefing model of Facts–Feelings–Future was initially used, as mentioned earlier, with professional rescue workers and emergency services personnel after major accidents and disasters. It has subsequently been used in the aftermath of a wide range of traumatic events and experiences, whether sudden and dramatic or of long duration, from international hostage situations to personal bereavement. In all such situations of actual or threatened major loss or change people can react with shock, anger, fear, guilt, shame, isolation or loss of self-esteem and confidence, or a combination of these. The model can be adapted for almost any incident where these reactions figure. Helping people to separate facts from feelings and emotions and identifying areas where further support is needed can go a long way towards enabling them to restructure difficult experiences and incorporate them into their lives.

The method's message is:

> Just stop for a moment. Control your feelings and put your emotional reactions on hold—there will be time for these later, when you have looked at what happened, why it happened and how you and others were involved. You can then look at your emotional reactions, at what you can do about them and at what help and support are available if you need them.

As well as being suitable (1) for people who are involved in traumatic situations over a long period of time, the model can also be used (2) in counselling, and (3) as a method of self-debriefing after even minor incidents.

1   USING DEBRIEFING FOR ON-GOING INCIDENTS

Police, fire and rescue and ambulance service personnel, doctors and nurses, social workers and clergy all experience not only incidents that are sudden, traumatic and short-lived, but also on-going situations that produce varying levels of stress.

With aid workers
Aid workers overseas often work in situations characterised by poverty, starvation, disease, death, war, drought and floods. Aid agencies continue to send doctors, water engineers, relief workers and others to such places as Rwanda, the Sudan and Bosnia.

Some are unprepared for the conditions in which they will have to live and work—in tents or primitive huts in the middle of a wilderness, cut off from the outside world except by telephone or radio. Because of organisational problems or the inherent chaos of the situation, the chain of command may not be clear and there may be no perceived or actual structures of responsibility or support. This can result in uncertainty about procedures and conflicts in personal relationships. In addition to the possibility of being threatened or killed, unfamiliar food or climate may compound the problems. Some aid workers find it difficult to relax and, because of the enormous needs of those amongst whom they work, often feel guilty when having time off or just resting, and this can lead to vulnerability and burn-out. Some have no psychological support while overseas; defusing and Debriefing are not available. The support that a team might offer may be non-existent; or, on the other hand, it may be resented. On returning home, some find it difficult to readjust to their home life or to work. And because of the multiple stresses that they have endured some fail to recognise that there have been, or still are, any problems.

Michael worked overseas for six months for a major aid agency. He believed that he had not experienced any distressing incidents. On his return he was seen by the occupational health department of the aid agency and offered a Critical Incident Debriefing, which he agreed to attend. He said at the beginning of the Debriefing that he had not been threatened and had not been involved in or seen any traumatic or horrifying incidents, but that he had come along because he had been told by others that it would be helpful.

The debriefer went through the normal Introduction and then on to the Facts Stage, and asked Michael how he had got the job. He said that he had replied to an advertisement in a newspaper and that within three weeks, with little preparation other than a medical and a practical briefing, he had arrived in the country where he was to work. He was given no psychological preparation or information about possible reactions that he might have. The debriefer asked him what his thoughts and expectations were before going, and then invited him to talk about how he got there, what his first impressions were, what happened when he arrived at the airport and how he got to his destination.

Michael began to talk quite casually, but as the Debriefing progressed he realised that, early on, incidents had happened that had been quite frightening but that he had forgotten. When he had arrived at the airport, without any explanation he had been taken by armed soldiers to a room where he was threatened and made to pay money before they would let him into the country. He realised that he had buried this incident and that he needed to talk about his feelings of shock and anger, and the fear that he could have been beaten up or shot.

He then began to talk about other incidents. One that had seemed trivial at the time, but had disturbed him, was being told to drive a vehicle on the understanding that if he hit another vehicle or ran anyone over he was not to stop because he might be killed in the ensuing riot by an angry mob. At the time, he had not realised the effect this had had on him, and now he felt guilty, angry and helpless about traffic incidents in which he had been involved. He also recalled that he had experienced loss of confidence and uncertainty when driving after he came home, and had not known why.

The debriefer asked him not to attempt the impossible task of talking through the whole six months, but to concentrate on the major events in which he had been involved during that time. Michael identified two other incidents when he had been frightened. He also remembered that his relationship with a senior member of staff had been difficult, and he still felt angry about it. Also, on his return he had not known why he had been irritated by his children asking for

248 Critical Incident Debriefing

money or sweets. In the Debriefing he saw that he was unconsciously comparing them with the starving children he had seen overseas. The Debriefing dealt with these experiences in turn, using the Facts and Feelings Stages in each case. The Debriefing concluded by looking at his journey home, what he thought about it and how he had been affected by it since.

By putting him through the Debriefing process, the debriefer enabled Michael to face up to experiences that had produced feelings and reactions that he had buried, and of whose influence and effect on his life he was unaware.

People who experience long-term situations characterised by varying levels of stress may, like those who find themselves involved in sudden traumatic incidents, be unaware of the connection between events and their reactions to them. Because they may have to endure such situations for weeks or months at a stretch, defences may operate at a high level, and they cope by constantly controlling and burying their feelings and emotions.

Having worked overseas as an aid worker for nine months, on her return June attended a Debriefing. She had lived with her colleagues many miles from the refugee camps in the comfort of a hotel, returning there each evening after spending a long day working with men, women and children who were dying from hunger and disease. She accepted that if she was to continue her work she had to survive, which meant living away from the camp, being fed and having a room and a bed. She felt that, compared with the refugees, she was living in luxury; but she had accepted this as the price that she, and they, had to pay for her work. She had been told, she said, that when driving about she was not to give any of the food she was carrying to the refugees—not even a packet of biscuits—otherwise, a riot might develop in which many might be killed.

In the Debriefing she talked about the constant feelings of guilt, despair and anger that she had felt at having to constantly suppress her normal reaction, which was to stop and help, especially when children were involved. She had been unaware of the strength of her feelings, and gradually began to talk about them and to express her emotions. After her return she had sometimes reacted to family and

Summary 8: The multi-incident Debriefing model

	Time flexible
Introduction	Aim, rules, procedure.
	'How did you get into your work?'
	'What expectations, and what preparation?'
	'What were your first impressions?'
	'What main incidents do you remember?'
	'How did you get involved in them?'
Incident 1 *Facts*	'What was happening *before* the incident?'
	'What were you thinking?' 'What did you do?'
	'What happened *during* the incident?'
	'What happened *after* the incident?'
Feelings	Sensory impressions.
	Feelings, emotions, reactions.
	'What has this incident left you with?'
Support	'What support did you have at the time?'
	'What support have you had since?'
Incident 2	
Incident 3	Dealt with in the same way as Incident 1.
Incident 4	
	'What are you feeling now?'
Future	Normalisation, information, support.
	Referral.
Ending	

friends, or at work, in ways that were out of character, and she had not known why.

The *technique* used with Michael and June is not to attempt to debrief the whole of the time, but to ask them to look at how they came to be involved and to recall the major events. The Debriefing deals with these in turn, as well as with their return journeys and their reactions since they came home. This means that between the Introduction and the Future Stage the Debriefing contains a number of mini-Debriefings, looking at facts and then feelings. An outline of the procedure is given in Summary 8. In the case of an aid worker, the debriefer asks in the Facts Stage:

'How did you get the job?'
'What preparation did you receive?'
'How did you get to the country and to your place of work?'
'What happened when you arrived, and on the way to your place of work?'
'What problems were there as far as living and working conditions were concerned, and in relationships?'

This period is then dealt with via the Feelings Stage.

Next, the debriefer focuses on the main incidents of the experience, and these are dealt with in turn, using the Facts and Feelings Stages and considering the support available at the time or later.

'What main incidents do you remember being involved in?'

The debriefer then asks:

'What did you think when you knew you were to come home?'
'What did you think when you left?'
'How did people treat you at work and at home when you returned?'
'What problems have you experienced since your return?'
'What do you think now?'

He continues by concentrating on feelings, then moves on to the Future Stage and Ending.

In some cases aid workers ask, or need, to be referred for counselling.

With emergency services personnel
As we have seen, professional rescuers, helpers and carers often experience on-going stress over long periods and are required to cope with recurring traumas. The cumulative effect of all this

can be disturbing. Some may argue that 'You just get used to it', or 'You become hardened to it in order to survive.' But others find that they begin to suffer physical and psychological reactions. A few will be retired early on medical grounds, having developed post-traumatic stress or PTSD, but some may not experience any reactions or effects until long after retirement. Simple and formal defusing and Critical Incident Debriefing aim to lessen these reactions. The technique used is identical to that outlined above for aid workers: a number of incidents are identified and dealt with in succession.

The debriefer needs to decide when the story should begin and, because this may mean going back a long time, he should discuss it beforehand with the debriefees. He begins by taking them back to a point when the situation was calm and normal, then moves through the Debriefing model using Summary 8 as a guide, dealing with each incident in turn.

Useful questions to ask:

'How did you come to be a police/fire and rescue/ambulance officer/etc.?'
'Why did you join, and what were your expectations?'
'How did these expectations work out?'
'Think of a time when things were calm and normal and describe what it was like then.'
'What incidents can you remember since then which were particularly difficult to handle?'
'What have these incidents left you with now?'

The incidents are tackled in turn by looking at the facts and the feelings, including what happened after each incident, but the Future Stage is omitted until all the incidents have been covered. The debriefer ends by bringing the debriefees into the present and conducting the usual Future Stage of normalisation, information, support and, where necessary, referral.

With other professionals

A similar procedure can be used with that same wide variety of people, frequently encountered in this book, who through their work sometimes suffer on-going and cumulative stress—doctors, social workers, bus drivers, traffic wardens ... —indeed, any who experience shock, anger or feelings of helplessness in their work, or aggression or threat from others, whether regularly or occasionally.

2   USING DEBRIEFING IN COUNSELLING

Although Debriefing is *not* counselling, the basic three-stage structure can be used within counselling. The counselling process involves the counsellee telling the story of what is happening and what has happened, looking at why it happened, and making decisions about what can be done. But the story rarely comes out in one logical sequence—it often consists of a number of different and sometimes complicated and confused episodes. The Debriefing model can help to put these different episodes into perspective by isolating them as single incidents and thus enabling the counsellee to see what effects and influences they have had. They can then be added to the overall picture of the experience, rather like the pieces of a jigsaw.

With couples or groups

With a couple, the facts and feelings are usually mixed together, and in telling his or her story each sometimes tries to maintain his or her own position and to blame the other, which results in confrontation. The various episodes can be dealt with using a mini-Debriefing model. The counsellor stays with the structure of Facts–Feelings–Future, but applies it to an individual story or experience within the counselling framework.

When Brian and Joan arrived at their third counselling session, Joan began by saying, 'We had a terrible row last night when Brian came in from work and have hardly spoken since then. He was in an awful mood and just flew off the handle when I asked him what sort of a day he'd had.' She related what had happened; Brian then became angry, tried to defend himself, and told his version of the story.

The counsellor asked them both to stop for a moment, explaining that it might help if they could look at this incident in a different way. She would like them each in turn, she said, to tell the story of what happened, but without bringing in feelings. She then asked them to go back to before the row started and to tell her what they were each doing before Brian came home.

Brian said he was driving home, and Joan said she was making the evening meal. Brian talked about what had happened at work and what he was thinking on his way home, and Joan spoke of being unwell and the children coming home from school and arguing and fighting. Each then talked about what happened when Brian walked into the house, and they concentrated on what they were doing and thinking, what they did and said and how the argument developed; all this time they kept their emotions and feelings submerged.

When the stories had been told, the counsellor moved on to look at sensory impressions and at the feelings and emotions that had emerged, and where they originated in the story, ending with what they felt now. This enabled the couple to stand back and view the argument, to understand how and why it had developed and how it had affected them, both when it had just happened and now. Brian saw that Joan had not been feeling well and had been angry with the children, and Joan understood that he had been worried about his work and the fear of redundancy, having had a difficult encounter with his boss. They also realised that other problems in their relationship were intruding. The mini-Debriefing helped them to understand what had happened and that they had both focused their anger and frustration on each other.

The counsellor does not abandon the counselling structure, but uses the model of Facts–Feelings–Future when an appropriate incident arises; such a mini-Debriefing would not take the three and a half hours or so allotted to a full Debriefing, but would be fitted into the time allowed for the counselling session.

With individuals
This mini-Debriefing process can also be used with individuals within counselling; again, the counsellor uses the Debriefing structure to deal with a particular incident.

John was extremely angry about what had happened with a senior colleague at work, and expressed his feelings during a counselling session. The counsellor asked him to go back to before the incident occurred and to explain what he was doing and thinking, without bringing in any emotions or feelings. John said that he was in his office preparing some work for a presentation that he was to give the next day; he was thinking, he said, that it was an important piece of work and that he had done his best, and he was looking forward to presenting it to the group. He expected to finish the work before he went home, so that he would be able to relax and not worry about it any more; he talked about what he was expecting to do that evening.

When the counsellor asked him what had happened to change things, John explained how his manager had come into the office, looked at what he had done, then observed that the presentation was not appropriate and would have to be changed. This had resulted in an argument, with both men growing very angry and aggressive. The counsellor worked through the Debriefing structure with John, asking him to give details about the incident up until the point when the manager had left the office, including the exact words each had used and how they had both reacted—all the time omitting the feelings. The counsellor then asked John to continue the story up to the point when he had gone home that evening and returned to work the next day. Next, he went back to the incident and asked about sensory impressions, which led to looking at the emotions and reactions that had emerged in the incident, as well as later.

The counsellor was already aware from the story that John had felt angry and humiliated by what had happened and by the way he had been treated. He felt he had been 'put down' and all his good work unnecessarily demeaned, because of an expectation on the part of his manager which should have been explained to him earlier. His confidence and self-esteem had been challenged and threatened.

By using this method, the counsellor became aware, as did

John, of the hidden agenda: John had not been promoted and bitterly resented his senior colleague—it became clear in the way John told the story that he thought him arrogant, and not as experienced or as skilled as himself. It was possible that the manager was aware of this and felt threatened by him. John was able to sort out some of the confusion and gained a clearer picture of what had happened and why, and what the possibilities were for the future.

3   SELF-DEBRIEFING

When the Debriefing structure is used by individuals to debrief themselves, the Facts–Feelings–Future model can help, as a self-analysis procedure, to create understanding of what happened and why, what the reactions were and what can be done about them. After many apparently minor but nonetheless disturbing incidents where the individual has felt confused and angry, helpless or afraid, he or she can sit down and work through the incident, applying the three-stage model.

Angus went into a shop to have a holiday film developed. A notice clearly stated that there was, among others, a one-hour service, for which a particular sum was charged. When he asked for this service, he was told that they were very busy and that the film would be ready in one and a half hours. He accepted this, and returned one and a half hours later to collect the photographs. When the assistant wanted to charge him at the one-hour rate, he objected, but was told that it was not the fault of the company, that they were busy, and that they were having problems with the machinery. Refusing to accept this explanation, he said that he was not going to pay the one-hour rate for a service that had taken one and a half.

The argument became heated, though Angus tried to keep his temper; but the situation escalated when the assistant became rude and abusive, then walked away. Angus demanded to see a supervisor. By now he was breathing hard and sweating, and was very angry at the dismissive and arrogant attitude of the assistant. With the intervention of the supervisor the situation was eventually resolved, and Angus paid at the two-hour rate. He left the shop still shaking, with his heart pounding, and although he felt that he had succeeded he also felt humiliated and was still very angry and upset.

When he got back to his car he sat quietly for a while, and went through the incident using the three-stage model: why had he gone into the shop and what was he thinking? what happened and why? what was said and done, by him and by the assistant? what happened when the supervisor came? what happened when it was over? He then moved on to feelings: how had he felt when he walked into the shop? how had he felt during the development of the argument? how was it resolved? how did he feel about it then, and what did he feel now? He realised that although he had experienced a highly charged emotional encounter in which he had felt exploited, he was left with the sense that his personal rights had been vindicated. As he drove away, he felt much more calm and relaxed.

Had Angus driven away immediately, he might have driven dangerously or carelessly and had an accident. Using the Debriefing model helped him to calm down, understand what had happened and put his experience into a better perspective.

There are many situations where the model can be used in this way to help create personal understanding: for instance, after arguments with partners, children, neighbours and colleagues; after difficult experiences in shops, offices, agencies, hospitals, schools and places of work; after distressing telephone conversations—and any other encounters which result in feelings of anger, fear, guilt, distress, bitterness, regret, isolation or humiliation.

FINAL COMMENTS

I hope that this book has helped to create interest in the methods of defusing and Critical Incident Debriefing. I believe that the Critical Incident Debriefing model has a sound theoretical basis in line with the way that our understanding of trauma and traumatic reactions has developed in the wake of experiences of war and disaster, and uses techniques common to many different kinds of approach to crisis intervention. The model offers a confidential environment in which individuals or groups can talk about their experiences and their reactions to them, as well as a clear structure in which to incorporate them. This structure can itself provide safety and new understanding, especially when people feel that their lives have been disrupted, disoriented or shattered. Most important of all, it offers a method of cognitive restructuring which should enable people to make better sense of their experiences and to integrate it into their lives.

Let Dr Atle Dyregrov have the last word:

By providing survivors, bereaved and helpers with rapid help, and by building on the internal strengths of the affected groups, we may prevent much of the unnecessary pain and agony experienced by these groups.

I certainly hope that we can prevent post-traumatic stress reactions in the future, not only by psychological debriefings, but by a better system for intervening in crisis situations. Hopefully, debriefings, in addition to other measures, can accelerate normal recovery and prevent post-traumatic stress disorder. (Dyregrov 1989)

Appendix A: The Three-stage Revised Model: The Debriefer's Guide

INTRODUCTION

Introduce yourself: give a short outline of your experience in conducting Debriefings. If present, the co-debriefer also gives a self-introduction.

Explain the purpose and aims

- To enable the group (or individual) to talk through the event so that any unwanted psychological or other effects will be reduced.
- To share experiences as a group.
- To allow ventilation of impressions, reactions and feelings.
- To help them to cognitively restructure the event in their minds and make better sense of the experience.
- To utilise the influences and strengths of the group (or individual) and to reduce tension.
- To mobilise resources—personal, family, group, organisational and external.
- To 'normalise' the situation and people's reactions, and to look to the future.
- To stress that *debriefing is not counselling.*

Explain the rules
Come to some agreement about *smoking*.

1 *No compulsion to speak*

- Pressure will not be put on anyone to answer questions if he or she does not wish to do so.

2 *Confidentiality* (rules to be agreed or negotiated)

- Nobody should talk to anyone outside the group about what has happened or been said by others in the Debriefing.
- No confidential or personal matters will be mentioned in any reports or discussions afterwards.
- What happens in the Debriefing is for the group to deal with. But where the law has been broken, the issue of confidentiality will need to be discussed.
- No one should disclose information during the Debriefing if he or she does not wish to do so.

3 *Complaints*
The Debriefing is neither investigative nor a forum for complaints, although some criticisms of the system or of individuals may arise.

4 *Personal matters*
Personal problems not related to the event will be acknowledged, but not dealt with in the Debriefing. The aim is to deal with the incident *now*.

5 *Feeling worse*
Some may feel worse during or at the end of the Debriefing, but this is normal. If anyone is upset, cries or leaves the room, the others will be asked to support him or her.

Explain the procedure
Explain the way the Debriefing will be conducted.

- *Questions* Each person, in turn, will be asked the same questions.
- *Emotional distancing* Facts and story first; emotions and feelings later. Give examples of how this can be done.

Any questions?
Ask the debriefees to state their *first name* and their *role* during the incident.

STAGE 1: THE FACTS

Build up a comprehensive picture of what each person was doing before he or she heard about the event. Concentrate on:

'What did you *expect*?'
'What did you *think*?'
'What did you *do*?'
'What *happened*?'

Before the incident

Ask each person, in turn, questions appropriate to the incident:

'Where were you before you heard about/became involved in the incident?'
'What was the weather like?' 'The road conditions/traffic/ people/crowds/hills/grass, etc.?'
'Who were you with?' 'What were you doing/talking about/ thinking about/listening to/looking at?'

During the incident

'How did you hear about the incident?'
'What *happened* and what did you *expect*?'
'Describe what you saw.'
'What did you *do*?'
'What did you *think* at the time?'

After the incident

Ask each person what happened when the incident was over:

'What happened when the police came and after they left?'
'How did the police/ambulance/hospital staff and others treat you?'
'What happened when you went home, and how were you treated?'
'What happened when you went to work the next day?'
'What reactions have you experienced since the incident?'

STAGE 2: THE FEELINGS AND EMOTIONS

Decide which method you are going to use:
1 The *specific method* (longer)—work through the reactions in chronological order.
2 The *general method* (shorter)—take an overall focused view, asking which reactions are dominant.

Sensory impressions
What did you *hear, see, smell, taste, touch*? What are your memories of these *now*?

Emotional reactions and feelings
Deal with:

- *Overt feelings* What feelings and emotions have already been mentioned in telling the story in the factual stage?
- *Covert feelings* What emotions were experienced, but hidden?

'What did you feel about what happened?'

'What do you feel *now*?' Ask about a selection of these:

FEAR. HELPLESSNESS. FRUSTRATION. ANGER. RAGE. GUILT. SADNESS. DEPRESSION. ANXIETY. UNPRE- PAREDNESS. SENSE OF UNREALITY. SENSE OF ABNOR- MALITY. SENSE OF LOSS. EMPTINESS. CONFLICT. POINTLESSNESS. BEING A PAWN IN A GAME. DETACH- MENT. SENSE OF TIME SLOWING DOWN. REJECTION. ISOLATION. 'WHY ME/HIM/HER/US?'

'When did you cry, feel angry or upset?'
'What did you feel about others around you (in the team or group)?'
'What did your family ask, or say to you?' 'How did you feel about this?'

'In what ways were their reactions *helpful* or *unhelpful*?'
'What was the worst thing for you about the incident?'
'What emotional and physical reactions have you had since the incident?'
'How do you feel as you sit here now?'
'Have there been any positive reactions, or lessons learned?'

STAGE 3: THE FUTURE

Normalisation
Emphasise the normality of any reactions.

Information
Talk about the possibility of further reactions:

- Intrusive thoughts and images.
- Increased feelings of anxiety and vulnerability.
- Irritability—with self, others, children, work, etc.
- Difficulty in concentrating.
- Inability to show feelings or emotions.
- Sleep disturbances—dreams or nightmares.
- Changes in the way the debriefees think, see themselves or view life in general—work, family, purpose, meaning, etc.

Help should be considered:

- If symptoms do not decrease after about 4–6 weeks (longer for a personal bereavement or other major loss).
- If symptoms increase over time.
- If there is loss of function or ability at home or work, or in personal relationships or life in general.
- If marked personality changes occur.

Ask whether there are any feelings of *growth* or *learning*?

'What, if anything, has this experience taught you?'

Support
What support is available?

- *Personal support*:   Who is available for each individual?
- *Group support*:   How can the group support each other?
- *Organisational support*:   What support is available within the organisation?
- *External resources*:   What outside agencies and local organisations are available?

Give out a list of people and helping groups or organisations, both internal and external, and their telephone numbers.

The aftermath
Are there to be identity parades, court cases, inquests, inquiries, hospital visits, funerals? Discuss the need for support during these. Is there a need for assessment at a later stage.

ENDING

Ask each member of the group to make a *final statement* about how he or she feels *now*, as he or she sits here after the Debriefing. The statement should be made *to the group*, not to the debriefer.

If appropriate, mention that refreshments will be provided. Stay for these, and be available.

Thank everyone for taking part, then end the session.

People can now return to work, stay for refreshments or go home.

- *Do any individuals need to be referred?*

Have an *informal talk with the senior person* responsible for the individual or group.

If appropriate, walk around the workplace and say goodbye to the debriefees.

Check your own need for supervision.

Appendix B: Treatment and Training Centres for PTS and PTSD

The individual should make contact, or be referred, via his or her GP. Many local hospitals and psychiatric clinics have a Traumatic Stress Clinic in their departments of psychology or psychotherapy. Local counselling agencies should have lists of therapists and counsellors specialising in trauma counselling and Debriefing.

The following offer therapy, Debriefing, counselling, help and advice.

Hospital and clinics
Department of Clinical Psychology, Haverstock House
St Anne's Road, Lincoln LN2 5RL
Tel: 01522 512512/Fax: 01522 546337

Department of Clinical Psychology, Withington Hospital, Manchester M20 8LR
Tel: 0161 4458111 (main switch board)/0161 2914058 (secretary)/Fax: 0161 2914319

Department of Clinical Psychology/Psychotherapy, Warneford Hospital
Headington, Oxford OX3 7JX
Tel: 01865 741717/Fax: 01865 226507

Duke's Priory Hospital (private)
Stumps Lane, Springfield, Chelmsford, Essex CM1 5SJ
Tel: 01245 345345/Fax: 01245 346177

Ticehurst House Hospital (private)
Ticehurst, Wadhurst, East Sussex TN5 7HU
Tel: 01580 200391/Fax: 01580 201006

Traumatic Stress Clinic (for UK-wide referrals via GP)
73 Charlotte Street, London W1P 1LB
Tel: 0171 436 9000/Fax: 0171 436 8800

Traumatic Stress Clinic, Institute of Psychiatry
Maudsley Hospital, De Crespigny Park,
Denmark Hill, London SE5 8AF
Tel: 0171 919 2969/Fax: 0171 919 3573

Ty Gwyn
21 Bryn y Bia Road, Craigside, Llandudno, Gwynedd LL30 3AS
Tel: 01492 544081 (24-hour help-line)

Military hospitals and clinics
Specialise in PTSD.

Defence Services Psychiatric Centre (DSPC), Duchess of Kent
Military Hospital
Catterick, North Yorkshire DL9 4DF
Tel: 01748 873058

Royal Naval Hospital
Department of Psychiatry, Haslar, Gosport, Hants PO12 2AA
Tel: 01705 584255/Fax: 01705 762205

Ex-service personnel
Ex-Services Mental Welfare Society (also known as Combat
Stress)
Broadway House, The Broadway, Wimbledon, London SW19
1RL
Tel: 0181 543 6333/Fax: 0181 542 7082
Has welfare officers throughout the UK, offering advice and
support for those suffering from combat stress. The British Legion
and other ex-service organisations also offer help and advice.

Other organisations and agencies
Offer help, support and advice and, in some cases, counselling
and referral.

Stresscare
The Co-ordinator, 20 Parkwood Road, Tavistock, Devon PL19
0HH
Tel/Fax: 01822 610546
also known as the PTSD association.

Trauma After-Care Trust (TACT)
Buttfields, The Farthings, Withington, Gloucester GL5 4DF
Tel: 01242 890306
Offers advice and help.

Victim Support (central office)
Cranmer House, 39 Brixton Road, London SW9 6DZ
Tel: 0171 735 9166/Fax: 0171 582 5712
Local groups contacted via telephone directory.

War Pensioners' Agency
Tomlinson House, Norcross, Blackpool, Lancashire FY5 3WP
Tel: 01253 858858
Has welfare officers in every area to offer advice and help.

**Post-trauma stress counselling and Critical Incident
Debriefing**
Centre for Crisis Psychology
Four Arches, Broughton Hall, Skipton, N. Yorkshire BD23 3AE
Tel: 01756 796383/Fax: 01756 796384

Frank Parkinson, Priory Associates
9 Priory Mead, Longcot, Oxon. SN7 7TJ
Tel/Fax: 01793 784406
An association of trained counsellors and therapists specialising
in trauma counselling and Psychological Debriefing. Consultancy
and training in PTS awareness, defusing and Critical Incident
Debriefing are offered.

Carole Spiers Associates
Gordon House, 83–5 Gordon Road, Stanmore, Middlesex HA7
3QR
Tel: 0181 954 1593/Fax: 0181 907 9290
Offers training and counselling in all aspects of stress and trauma.

Organisations for those interested in trauma and counselling
British Association for Counselling (also offers advice)
1 Regent Place, Rugby, Warwickshire CV21 2PJ
Tel: 01788 550899/Fax: 01783 562189
Publishes a resources directory with a list of trauma specialists
and counsellors, and a training directory.

European Society for Traumatic Stress Studies (ESTSS)
C/o Traumatic Stress Clinic, 73 Charlotte Street, London W1P
1LB
Tel: 0171 436 0285/Fax: 0171 436 8800
Members are sent bulletins and the *Journal of Traumatic Stress*.
Conferences are organised in the UK and overseas.

Appendix C: References and Further Reading

Alexander, D. A., and Wells, A. (1990). Post-traumatic stress reactions among police officers after the Piper Alpha disaster. Paper given at the 2nd European Conference on Traumatic Stress, The Netherlands.

Antonovsky, A. (1987). *How People Manage Stress and Stay Well.* San Francisco: Jossey-Bass.

Appel, J. W. (1966). Preventive psychiatry. In Glass, A. J., and Bernucci, R. J. (eds), *Neuropsychiatry in World War II.* Washington, DC: US Government Printing Office, pp. 373–415.

Bandura, A. (1982). Self-efficacy mechanisms in human agency. *American Psychologist,* 37, 122–47.

Barker, Pat (1992). *Regeneration.* London: Penguin Books.

Barker, Pat (1994). *The Eye in the Door.* London: Penguin Books.

Berne, Eric (1968). *Games People Play.* London: Penguin Books.

Bettelheim, Bruno (1988). *The Informed Heart.* London: Pelican Books.

Blake, D. D. (1993). Treatment outcome research on PTSD. *NCP Clinical Newsletter,* 3, 14–17.

Caplan, G. (1964). *Principles of Preventive Psychiatry.* New York: Basic Books.

Davidson, J., Swartz, M., and Storck, M. (1985). A diagnostic and family study of PTSD. *American Journal of Psychiatry,* 142.

Diagnostic and Statistical Manual of Mental Disorders IV (1994)

(*DSM IV*). Washington, DC: American Psychiatric Association.

Dyregrov, A. (1989). Caring for helpers in disaster situations: psychological Debriefing. Paper presented at survival seminar, Tavistock Clinic, London, 3 March 1989. Also published in *Disaster Management*, 2(1).

Dyregrov, A., and Mitchell, J. T. (1992). Work with traumatized children—psychological effects and coping strategies. *Journal of Traumatic Stress*, 5(1).

Egan, Gerard (1990). *The Skilled Helper*. Belmont, California: Brooks/Cole.

Gleser, G. C., Green, B. L., and Winget, C. (1981). *Prolonged Psychological Effects of Disaster: A Study of Buffalo Creek*. New York: Academic Press.

Goleman, D. (1996). *Emotional Intelligence*. London: Bloomsbury Publishing.

Green, B. L. (1994). Psychological research in traumatic stress, an update. *Journal of Traumatic Stress*, 7, 341–62.

Green, D. (1986). The origins of resilience. In *Changes*, pp. 276–8.

Harig, Paul T., and Sprenger, William D. (1995). Factors of man-made stresses: terrorism, torture and combat. Paper presented at mental health conference in Kuwait, April 1995.

Harris, Thomas (1973). *I'm OK—You're OK*. London: Pan Books.

Helzer, J. E., Robins, L. N., and McEvoy, L. (1987). Post-traumatic stress disorder in the general population. *New England Journal of Medicine*, 317, 1630–34.

Herman, J. L. (1992). *Trauma and Recovery*. New York: Basic Books.

Hetherington, A., and Guppy, A. (1990). Post-traumatic stress reactions in the British police. Paper given at the 2nd European Conference on Traumatic Stress, The Netherlands.

Hodgkinson, P., and Stewart, M. (1991). *Coping with Catastrophe*. London: Routledge.

Holmes, R. (1985). *Acts of War: The Behaviour of Men in Battle*. New York: Free Press.

Janoff-Bulman, R. (1985). The aftermath of victimization: rebuilding shattered assumptions. In Figley, C. R. (ed.), *Trauma and Its Wake*, vol. 1. New York: Brunner Mazel.

Keane, T. M., Fairbank, J. A., Caddell, J. M., and Zimmering, R. T. (1989). Implosive (flooding) therapy reduces symptoms of post-traumatic stress disorder in Vietnam veterans. *Behaviour Therapy*, 16, 9–12.

Keegan, J. (1991). *The Face of Battle*. London: Pimlico.

Kobasa, S. C. (1979). Stressful life events, personality and health: an enquiry into hardiness. *Journal of Personality and Social Psychology*, 37, 1–11.

Kulka, R. A., Schlenger, W. E., Fairbank, J. A., Hough, R. L., Jordan, K., Marmar, C. and Weiss, D. S. (1990). National Vietnam Readjustment Study. New York: Brunner Mazel.

Lindemann, E. (1944). Symptomatology and management of acute grief. *American Journal of Psychiatry*.

McCammon, S., Durham, T. W., Allison, E. J., and Williams, J. E. (1988). Emergency workers' cognitive appraisal and coping with traumatic events. *Journal of Traumatic Stress*, 1, 353–72.

McCann, L., and Pearlman, L. A. (1990). *Psychological Trauma and the Adult Survivor: Theory, Therapy and Transformation*. New York: Brunner Mazel.

McCann, L., Sakheim, D. K., and Abrahamson, D. J. (1988). Trauma and victimization; a model of psychological adaptation. *Counselling Psychologist*, 16, 531–94.

McManners, H. (reprinted 1994). *The Scars of War*. London: HarperCollins.

Meichenbaum, D. (1994). *A Clinical Hand-book/Practical Therapist Manual for Assessing and Treating Adults with PTSD*. Waterloo, Ontario, Canada: Institute Press.

Mitchell, J. T. (1983). When disaster strikes—the Critical Incident Stress Debriefing process. *Journal of Emergency Medical Services*, 8(1)36–9.

Mitchell, J. T., and Everly, G. S. (1995). *Critical Incident Stress Debriefing: An Operations Manual for the Prevention of Traumatic Stress among Emergency Services and Disaster*

Workers. Ellicott City, Maryland: Chevron Publishing Corporation.

Muss, D. C. (1991). *The Trauma Trap.* New York: Doubleday.

Parkinson, F. W. (1992). Stress in social work teams in a county Social Services department. Unpublished paper.

Parkinson, Frank (1993a). *Post-Trauma Stress.* London: Sheldon Press.

Parkinson, Frank (1995). *Listening and Helping in the Workplace.* London: Souvenir Press. (Chapters on stress, post-trauma stress and Debriefing.)

Pearlin, L. I., Menaghan, E. G., Lieberman, M. A., and Mullan, J. T. (1981). The stress process. *Journal of Health and Social Behaviour.*

Pincus, Lily (1976). *Death and the Family.* London: Faber & Faber.

Putkowski, J., and Sykes, J. (5th impression 1993). London: Pen & Sword Books.

Quarantelli, E. L. (1985). The consequences of traumatic events. In, Figley, C. R. (ed.), *Trauma and Its Wake.* New York: Brunner Mazel.

Raphael, B. (1986). *When Disaster Strikes.* London: Hutchinson.

Raphael, B., and Meldrum, L. (1995). Does Debriefing after psychological trauma work? *British Medical Journal*, 310 (10 June 1995).

Rivers, W. H. R. (1918). The repression of war experience. *Lancet*, 2 Feb. 1918.

Rivers, W. H. R. (1923). *Conflict and Dream.* London: Kegan Paul.

Rotter, J. B. (1966). Generalised expectancies for internal versus external control of reinforcement. Psychological Monographs, 80, 1-28.

Scheier, M. F., and Carver, C. S. (1987). Dispositional optimism and physical well-being: the influence of generalized outcome expectancies on health. *Journal of Personality*, 55, 169–210.

Scheier, M. F., and Carver, C. S. (1992). Effects of optimism on psychological and physical well-being. *Cognitive Therapy and Research*, 16, 201–28.

Scott, M. J., and Stradling, S. G. (1992). *Counselling for Post-traumatic Stress Disorder*. London: Sage Publications.

Shapiro, F. (1989). Efficacy of the eye-movement desensitization procedure in the treatment of trauma memories. *Journal of Traumatic Stress*, 2, 199–223.

Tedeschi, R. G., and Calhoun, L. G. (1995). *Trauma and Transformation*. London: Sage Publications.

Tehrani, N., and Westlake, R. (1994). Debriefing individuals affected by violence. *Counselling Psychology Quarterly*, 7(3).

Ursano, R. J., Fullerton, C. S., and McCaughey, B. G. (1994). *Trauma and Disaster. Individual and Community Responses to Trauma and Disaster: The Structure of Human Chaos*. Cambridge University Press.

Van der Kolk, B. A., and van der Hart, O. (1991). The intrusive past: the flexibility of memory and the engraving of trauma. *American Images*, 48, 425–54.

Index